The Coconut Wireless

A Travel Adventure in Search of the Queen of Tonga

For Fluffanella.

Copyright

The Coconut Wireless: A Travel Adventure in Search of The Queen of Tonga

ISBN: 9780645118704
Imprint: Simon Michael Prior
10 9 8 7 6 5 4 3 2 1

Copyright © 2021 by Simon Michael Prior

All rights reserved. No part of this book may be reproduced or transmitted in any form or by any means without written permission from the author.

Contents

0.
Marooned

We are the only humans left on the island.

Crouched on the sand, staring at invisible ripples of water.

Black.

No moon, no stars, no lights, no electricity.

Hot.

Humid.

Giant, tusked wild pigs grunt and crash through the dense jungle behind us.

We huddle as the noise comes closer.

No way to leave the island.

No way to escape.

It will not be daylight again for almost twelve hours.

1.
Deportation

"Fiona, what do you mean, your visa's run out?"

"I mean, I can't stay in England. I have to go home to New Zealand."

"But I don't want you to go. We've just moved in together. You can't go."

"I don't have any choice, Simon. If they stamp 'overstayer' in my passport, I'll never be able to come back here."

"Woah. How long's left on the visa?"

"I just looked; it runs out today, May 4th, 1996. I'm going to walk up to the High Street travel agent as soon as they open, and try to book a flight."

My head in my hands, I processed this sudden change in our circumstances. We were both in our twenties; we had a flat together; we were planning a future in London. Deportation didn't feature anywhere in this strategy.

She can't just leave. And what's she going to do in New Zealand? Fiona's a city girl; she won't want to work on her parents' farm.

I had a thought. My Australian friend had found a way round his visa issues and was still living here. I rang him.

"Tommo, how ya doing?"

"Err, good, Simon. Sorry, I was dead to the world. Had a big one last night. Hang on, I'll just go to the kitchen phone, err… Sarah's still sleeping."

I heard a female voice in the background. "My name's not Sarah!"

The kitchen phone clicked.

"This is an early call, Simon. Is everything okay? How's it going, shacked up with that hot Kiwi chick?"

"Not good today. She's leaving."

"What d'ya mean, she's leaving? What have you done?"

"I've done nothing, Tommo. She's not allowed to stay any longer. Her visa ran out."

"Bummer, Simon. She was a good catch."

"She still is a good catch, Tommo. I need your help. How come you're still here? Your visa ran out too, didn't it?"

"I'm not here for long. I'm going back to Perth next month."

"So, are you in England illegally?"

"Yeah, nah."

Aussies are incomprehensible. What the hell did 'Yeah, nah' mean? Was that a yes or a no?

The same female voice shrieked so close to the phone I could taste the venom.

"Bastard. Don't ever contact me again."

A door slammed. Tommo's love life continued on its normal trajectory.

"Tommo, listen to me. Do you have a visa? I need to know how you found a way to stay here."

"It was easy. I went to France."

"Where does France come into this?"

"My two-year working holiday visa ran out, so I crossed to France for a few days, then they let me back into England for another six months as a tourist. Mind you, I got so smashed on cheap, duty-free beer they almost didn't let me in. D'ya know Victoria Bitter's £10 a crate there? I should've stayed longer. There was this one night, right, me and Dean were so pissed we ended up falling asleep in this field, and there was this giant bull, right, and…"

"Tommo, Tommo, that's great. We'll catch up for some more beers, but I need to sort this visa stuff out first. Thanks, you've been a great help. We'll see each other before you leave for Perth. Promise."

I turned to my girlfriend. She was still in her pyjamas, kneeling on our bed looking at me. Her head was on one side, halfway to touching her shoulder, her face a question mark. Dark red hair cascaded down her front.

You look stunning.

"Fiona, you know how you've always wanted me to take you to Paris? I was wondering, would you be free to go this afternoon?"

≈ ≈ ≈

Grey sky hung over Waterloo railway terminus as we ate station platform sandwiches served from clear plastic, triangular dinnerware. Fiona twirled me round and grinned like a Colgate toothpaste advert while the Eurostar train pulled in, and a multitude of uninterested professional people disembarked, dispersing over the concourse. We selected our seats, stuffed our small bags into the luggage space, and waited.

"I can't believe this morning I was out of my mind with worry I was going to overstay my British visa," said Fiona, "and now we're on a train to Paris. How random is that? This is amazing."

Fiona's enthusiasm lifted my mood. I'd visited Paris many times in my life and had seen almost every one of its temptations. France would buy us some breathing space—six months to be precise—but it delayed the inevitable outcome: Fiona had to go home to New Zealand.

The depressing rear ends of South London terraced houses passed by as the train quietly began its journey. A pause a short distance outside the station allowed passengers the benefit of viewing a buxom lady hanging out pillowcase-sized bras on a roof terrace washing line.

"Penny for your thoughts?" Fiona looked at me, concerned. "This is so exciting. I can't believe it's real."

"I don't want you to go home. I need to find a way we can stay together."

"Stop worrying, Simon. It'll work out."

"It works out because I work it out; stuff doesn't happen by itself. I have to think these things through."

"Please don't spoil our trip to Paris, worrying the whole time. It might be the only opportunity we get to go there together."

I sat back in my seat. Fiona read her magazine.

I need time to digest this. Please understand.

We exited the Channel Tunnel into the French night, speeding through invisible countryside.

A few lingering passengers remained in the evening on the Gare du Nord platforms. The station snack bar had run out of almost everything, and we grabbed two remaining, dried-up muffins manufactured in approximately the same year as the Mona Lisa.

I realised, in our rush to make sure Fiona was out of England before immigration affixed the dreaded 'overstayer' stamp in her passport, we'd failed to book any accommodation. Paris drizzle reflected my mood as we exited the station. Fiona skipped down the pavement, reminding me of Gene Kelly and his *Singin' in the Rain*. She stared, entranced, into shop windows.

Several station hotels presented various stages of dilapidation; their heavy drapes pulled closed like unwelcoming folded arms.

"Why are all these hotels advertising they're complete?" asked Fiona. "Are there lots of half-built ones or something?"

I laughed, despite my mood. She could always cheer me up. I had the advantage of having learnt French at school. Fiona's classes taught Maori.

"It says *complet*. It means they're full," I said. "No vacancies."

"None of them have any vacancies."

"I know; we should have booked ahead."

"Be reasonable; you did whisk me here at short notice."

"Be reasonable; you did tell me your visa was running out the same day it actually ran out."

Fiona looked at me far too enthusiastically. I knew that look—the one she gave me in the taxi on the way home from a nightclub.

"Be happy, Simon," she cajoled. "We're in Paris, the most romantic city on earth."

I didn't feel romantic.

She threw her arms round my neck.

"Let's find somewhere to have some Champagne."

"Champagne? Are you for real? Fiona, we need to find a place to stay."

"Come on, in here!"

2.
Champagne

Stacked-up wicker chairs stood wet and unloved outside a pavement café. Fiona grabbed my hand and pulled me out of the rain and in through a glass door. A luxurious black moustache holding a broom greeted us. Spectacles dangled from the moustache owner's neck. His expression wasn't welcoming.

"*Désolé. Nous sommes fermés.*"

Fiona's expression showed her incomprehension of his French.

"Sorry, I am closed," said the moustache.

"Please…"

She has this wonderful, innocent, childlike way about her that can persuade complete strangers to inconvenience themselves.

"We only want a glass of Champagne," she said, "it's our first night in Paris, please…"

His expression softened.

"You may 'ave a Champagne while I clean up. Sit down 'ere, and I will bring it."

One pair of bar stools weren't yet upside down on a table. We pulled them out and parked our backsides.

"Fiona, this isn't helping us find somewhere to stay."

"I know, but isn't it exciting? We're in Paris, and we're going to be drinking Champagne."

There was no choice of Champagne. The proprietor had brought us the end of an earlier diner's bottle.

I watched the rain dribble down the café window.

"Cheers, big ears!" said Fiona, thrusting her full Champagne flute in my direction. "To a shiny new visa. And to us."

Will there be any more than six months of 'us' left? That's all the new visa will provide.

"Simon, don't worry. Something will turn up."

That was how we always lived. I planned years ahead; she lived by the seat of her pants. And somehow, it worked for both of us.

But at 10:30 in the evening, we still didn't have a bed for the night.

≈ ≈ ≈

The proprietor had his back to us, cleaning the floor, swishing his mop around the small square tables.

"Excuse me, can you help us?" Fiona asked him. "We've just arrived in Paris; we've nowhere to sleep tonight, and all the hotels are full. We don't know what to do. Do you know anywhere we can stay?"

I couldn't believe her forwardness. This man was a café owner, a grumpy café owner who wanted to finish his cleaning and go home. He wasn't a tourist information service.

He leant his mop against the wall and looked at us. His mouth turned down, and his moustache tips raised up. He shrugged, a big, gallic movement using his entire body and arms.

"I 'ave some friends. I will call them."

He stepped behind the café counter, lifted his spectacles to his head, and studied a small book, running his finger down the pages. He picked up the phone handset from the wall and dialled.

We sipped our Champagne.

On the phone, a stream of French issued from under the moustache. My schoolboy language skills wouldn't let me understand any of it except '*Ce sont des étrangers*'. Great. I wasn't used to being on the receiving end of the word 'foreigner'.

The proprietor replaced the handset.

"I 'ave found someone who will help you."

This was extraordinary. Fiona looked at me, triumph evident.

"Walk a few minutes to Rue Turgot. There is a children's bookshop. An old man will be standing outside. You can stay with him."

Fiona leant across the counter.

"Thank you so much. How do we find Rue Turgot?"

The proprietor sighed, picked up a paper menu, and drew a simple map with a pencil.

"It's five minutes, easy to find. But go now; he'll be waiting."

We tipped back the Champagne and grabbed our bags.

"I'm so glad we found you," said Fiona. "I don't know what we'd have done."

"It's okay, but before you leave, it's 35 francs for the Champagne. The reservation service is *gratuit* (free)."

Oops.

Embarrassed, I paid him, and we headed out into the wet night.

≈ ≈ ≈

"Fiona, we can't stay with some random old man."

"Do you have any better ideas?"

"Let's keep looking for a hotel."

"Simon, it's 11 o'clock. It's dark; it's wet. I'm tired, and now I'm light-headed from the Champagne. Let's at least find the old man and suss him out."

We rounded the corner into Rue Turgot. Dim streetlights reflected on the pavements. Parked cars lined both sides, and light from a single shop spilt out. To my surprise, a tall, thin man stood outside. He wore a brimmed hat and a long cloak and held a walking stick.

"Hallo," said Fiona. "Are you the man we can stay with?"

He shook his head and beckoned us into an open doorway. I realised his head shake suggested he spoke no English.

I'm not sure about this.

Narrow stairs creaked under the old man's feet as he ascended. Fiona followed him, turning to me and smiling. The warm air wafting down welcomed us, and we began to steam like kettles.

On the first floor, our footsteps echoed on bare floorboards as we entered a high-ceilinged room, full of the homely smell of central heating and recently baked bread. Laundry hung from a contraption near a cast-iron cooking range. Through its glass front, we could see a fire burning like a coal advertisement.

A stout lady sat at a massive farmhouse table, a white apron with a pink border covering her front and a silver cross around her neck. She wore her grey hair in a bun, pulled back behind steel-rimmed, circular spectacles.

"*Bonsoir* (Good evening)," she greeted us.

She pushed down on the table to help herself stand and gestured towards a doorway behind her.

Knick-knacks covered the top of a dresser; china dolls sat in a rocking chair; teddies dressed in Victorian clothes filled the corners of the room, and soft, fluffy cushions and throws with lacy edges covered a metal-framed double bed. We'd entered a Laura Ashley catalogue. Fiona turned to the old lady.

"It's perfect. Thank you."

The lady smiled and nodded. She mimed the height of a bottle of water with two hands flat, one above the other.

"*Voulez-vous de l'eau?*"

I remembered my French. Did we want water?

"*Merci bien, Madame, et merci pour la chambre.* (Thank you, Madam, and thanks for the room.)"

"*De rien* (You're welcome)," she replied and disappeared to fill a bottle.

Fiona waltzed around the room, feeling the cushions and picking up the dolls.

"See, I told you everything would work out."

≈ ≈ ≈

The lady returned with the water and two glasses.

"*Frühstück?*"

Frühstück? *That's not a French word.*

Hang on, *Frühstück* was German. Translated literally it meant 'early piece'. Breakfast. She must have thought we spoke German.

I accepted her offer of breakfast and explained we were very definitely not German but from England and New Zealand.

"Ahh, *Nouvelle-Zélande.*" She nodded and smiled. It was clear she had no idea where it was.

Bed and breakfast. We'd fallen on our feet.

The pink bathroom next door had a wooden stool covered in little glass bottles. Translating some of the labels to ensure I didn't accidentally shampoo myself with hydrochloric acid, I chose an appropriate elixir and showered off the smell of travel.

A green, fluffy towel embraced me, and I found Fiona sitting on the bed, feet tucked under her legs, flicking through a red-covered hardback book.

"What's that you're reading, Fiona? Is it an old diary?"

"It's the guest book, Simon; have a read of this."

She showed me the entries on the final page, as recent as last week.

'*Thank you so much for your hospitality. We were desperate for somewhere to stay; everywhere was full. I can't remember how we discovered you, but I'm so glad we did.*' Mark and Karen, Toronto.

'*At midnight, you were able to take us in when we'd nowhere to stay. So grateful, and breakfast was delicious.*' Sue and David, Brisbane.

'*We'd have slept at the railway station if we hadn't found you. Thank you for saving us.*' Moshe and Limor, Tel Aviv.

Via a chain of random, unconnected happenings, Fiona had steered us to the Mother Theresa of Paris.

≈ ≈ ≈

Paris, Paris, Paris. The city of romance. The city of love. The city of rain. It rained continuously. It rained heavily. Dark-coated Parisians hurried past, hidden under black umbrellas, stepping round shallow lakes forming on the pavements.

Fiona's wide eyes marvelled at the shop windows in the Champs-Élysées, the bright lights of Louis Vuitton and Guerlain enticing her into their evil, money-masticating embraces.

"This is sooo exciting," she said. "Can we go up the Eiffel Tower?"

"Now? In this weather?"

"What's wrong, Simon? You've had something on your mind ever since we've been here. Can't you relax and enjoy the moment?"

"I'm sorry. I can't stop thinking about how you'll go home in six months. This rain doesn't exactly fill me with the joys of spring either."

"What can we do about the weather?"

"Nothing."

"Exactly. And while we're here in Paris, what can we do about me having to go home?"

"Nothing, I suppose."

"Right. Stop thinking about it, and let's enjoy our time here. It'll be over before we know it."

The vast, metal climbing frame of the Eiffel Tower stood over us as we gazed upward, watching the illusion of the tower falling over with the motion of the clouds.

"Shall we take the lift or the stairs?" I asked.

"The stairs, I think. There's a big queue for the lift tickets. Plus, it's cheaper."

Fiona raced ahead, and I struggled to follow.

I caught up with her at the second level.

"What…what's the rush? Can we have a rest?"

"I think this is as far as we can climb. A little lift goes to the top. I'll buy the tickets while you recover, you old man."

We were glad of the cage around the top platform. Horizontal rain stung our faces as we struggled to stand up. Fiona asked a fellow tourist to take a picture of us. He snapped four, completely failing to take one without Fiona's red hair blowing all over her face.

We're making memories, but we've only got six months of memories left to make.

I hoped I was keeping these thoughts hidden.

It was noon by the time we reached the ground. We needed to shelter from the rain, which threatened to penetrate to my underpants.

"Did you know, lunchtime in France can last from twelve until two? Shall we find a café?"

"Definitely," said Fiona. "I want to try frogs' legs." She beamed and took my hand.

I love your spirit. I want to be with you for ever.

≈ ≈ ≈

We spent the weekend in Paris, the city of love. The rain didn't spoil our wonderful couple time. But the visa predicament refused to fade away.

We found our way back to the Gare du Nord and encountered the barricades of British border control before we were allowed to board the train.

"Passports, please."

A skinny lady with short black hair perched behind the immigration kiosk. Glasses balanced halfway down her pointed nose. Her mouth was in a straight line as she inspected us. My British passport didn't interest her, and she waved me to one side. She held up Fiona's New Zealand passport and looked first at the passport, then at Fiona, then back at the passport. She flicked through the pages. I bit my nails.

"You've been in Britain for two years on your working holiday visa?"

She had a strong Scottish accent.

"Yes," said Fiona.

"And your visa has now expired."

"Yes."

"Why, then, are you entering Britain again?"

Oh shit.

3.
A French Kiss

Fiona smiled at the immigration lady.

"There are parts of the country I didn't visit. I travelled round most of England and Wales, even Ireland, but I've never seen Scotland, and I've heard it's the most beautiful part. Please may I have more time to experience Scotland before I return home?"

I couldn't believe it. Fiona had picked up that the immigration lady was from Scotland, and she was flattering her.

"Could I please see your onward ticket to New Zealand?"

This wasn't going well. I knew Fiona didn't have one.

Fiona's expression became sheepish. "I haven't booked it yet. I'll do so as soon as I return to London. I promise."

She lowered her voice, and the immigration lady had to lean forward across the desk to hear, turning her head to one side.

"I wasn't sure you were going to allow me in. It's such a relief you're a nice, friendly Scottish lady. I thought I was going to have to deal with one of those rude Englishmen."

I covered my eyes with my hand and looked down.

Oh no, this isn't the way to speak to border control.

A flicker of a smile crossed the Scottish lady's face. She immediately recovered her stern, official composure.

"I'm not supposed to do this, but I'm going to give you a six-month tourist visa. But you must book your onward ticket this week; you can't stay without one."

Fiona clapped and grinned.

"I will. I promise. Thank you so much. You've been amazing."

Wow. Fiona's naïve, innocent demeanour had earned her a visa, just as it had persuaded the French café owner to find us a room, which now seemed like weeks ago.

The immigration lady's stamp thumped on Fiona's passport. She beckoned Fiona closer, and I could barely make out her voice.

"When you travel to Scotland, try to visit Aberdeen. It's where I come from, and it's known for its beauty."

"Of course. I'll make sure I do. Thank you."

I hurried Fiona away before the lady changed her mind, and we boarded the Eurostar for our return trip to London. Fiona had a brand-new, six-month tourist visa in her passport, and for the time being, she was legal.

"I thought you'd been to Scotland already?" I asked.

"I have, twice. Her precious Aberdeen's nothing special."

≈ ≈ ≈

There was no room on the Eurostar train for us to sit beside each other. Next to me was a plump, middle-aged man in a pale suit. He sniffed constantly, and I didn't enjoy our proximity. Fiona's neighbour was a teenage boy, immersed in a magazine about rock music.

My mind was back on the problem of our impending separation.

Outside, grey skies covered the flat, featureless French countryside speeding past.

I looked at Fiona over the melamine table between us.

"How about if I came with you to New Zealand?" I said.

Her eyes widened.

"Say that again?"

"How about if I came with you to New Zealand?"

"What, for ever?"

"I don't know about for ever. For now."

"But what about your job?"

"It's not exactly a career, is it? It pays the bills. There'll be other jobs."

"Wow. Okay. Gosh. What would you do in New Zealand?"

"No idea. I'll find something. We've got six months to save some money."

"Seriously?"

"Seriously."

The reality of my proposal sank in. Fiona flung her hair back, lunged at me across the table, and kissed me open-mouthed, as if we were in the ultimate scene of one of the more pornographic 1960s romantic movies. The fat man squished up against the train window. The teenager disappeared into the folds of his magazine. We didn't care. We loved each other, and now there was a way we could be together.

We just had to make it happen.

≈ ≈ ≈

"Hello, is that the High Street travel shop? I want to inquire about getting a flight to New Zealand. Yes, New Zealand. No, it's not in Europe. Not something you specialise in? Okay, thank you."

"Hello, yes, do you sell flights to New Zealand? No, I don't want to go to Sydney; that's not in New Zealand. Not something anyone's asked you for before? Okay, thanks, bye."

"Hello, can you sell me a flight to New Zealand? No, not a package tour, I just need flights. You only sell packages? Okay, thank you."

"This is impossible, Fiona. Everybody wants to sell me two weeks in an all-inclusive hotel in Benidorm."

"There's a shop in Paddington where my friend bought flights last month. She was going on an expedition to South-East Asia. I think they're called Travel Unlimited? She was pretty impressed with them."

"Paddington? Central London. Okay, let's try them."

I found their number in the *Yellow Pages*.

"Hello, is that Travel Unlimited? Do you sell flights to New Zealand? You do? Which way round do I want to go?" I turned to Fiona. "He's asking me which way round we want to go?"

"Let's go via America. I haven't been there before."

"America, please. Although thinking about it, can I come in and have a chat with you? You're the first travel agent I've spoken to who knows where New Zealand is."

≈ ≈ ≈

The shop front of Travel Unlimited fascinated me. Posters for backpacking in South America and tropical scuba diving in Asia decorated the window, and inside, several young people sat at desks, behind computer terminals, speaking into headsets.

A young, blonde lady stood near the door, her grey polo shirt carrying the company's logo.

"Hi, how can I help?"

I like her South African accent.

"I've got an appointment with Ben. I spoke to him on the phone earlier."

"This way; he's just finishing a call. He won't be long. Have a seat."

Ben spoke importantly into his headset as he sat behind his desk. We were about the same age. Square trendy glasses were stuck on his head, irretrievably tangled in his dark, unruly hair. He finished his call and smiled at me.

"Hi, Simon, is it? And you want to go to New Zealand?"

"Yes, my girlfriend Fiona's from there. Her visa runs out in a few months, and she has to go home. I seem to have decided I'm going with her."

"Good move; my girlfriend's a Kiwi too. Okay, let's examine your options. You said you'd prefer to go via America?"

"Yes, I've been there before, but Fiona hasn't, and she loves experiencing new countries."

"Great. Well, if you fly Air New Zealand via Los Angeles, you'll be able to visit some other places too. You could go via Hawaii, and on to Samoa, or Fiji, for instance."

"Wow, I didn't know there were that many choices to make."

Ben uncoupled his glasses from tentacles of fringe with some difficulty and clicked at his keyboard.

"There's a flight here that'd suit you. Air New Zealand to Los Angeles, then to Hawaii, then to Samoa, then to Auckland. Is Fiona from Auckland?"

"She's not; she's from the South Island."

"You'd have to change planes again. I can add on a flight to Christchurch for the same amount of money."

"That sounds fantastic—three fresh new places. I wonder what Samoa's like. I don't know anything about it."

Ben studied his screen closely.

"You don't have to go via Samoa. There's also an option to fly from Hawaii to New Zealand via Tonga."

Tonga.

I hadn't heard Tonga mentioned since my childhood.

4.
Linger Longer, Queen of Tonga

My mind drifted back to my boyhood bedroom.

Cross-legged on the floor in my new school uniform, I unpacked the unfamiliar pile of books ready for me to start the next year at primary school. I loved the shiny feeling, the un-dogeared perfection.

I opened *Adventures in Geography* at a photograph of a family in front of a straw hut, surrounded by palm trees.

A man holding a spear and wearing a skirt. A seated lady, four bare-chested, grinning brown children, and two spotty pigs.

One word under the picture.

Tonga.

I showed the picture to my father.

"Dad, can we go to Tonga?"

"Tonga?"

"Have you ever been to Tonga, Dad?"

"I haven't, but I saw the Queen of Tonga once."

Was she the lady with the pigs in my book?

My father leant back in his chair, removed his spectacles, and cleaned them.

"It must be over twenty years ago now. I stood in the crowd at our Queen Elizabeth's coronation, waiting all night in the rain with your grandmother. As the procession passed by, the visiting kings and queens huddled inside their closed carriages. I couldn't see any of them. It was such a shame about the weather."

"What happened next, Dad?"

"People began shouting and clapping. An open carriage approached, and behind the driver and footman, a handsome lady waved with her bare arms at everybody. We cheered and cheered. I raised my Union Jack as high as I could, and she looked right at me and grinned. I didn't know who she was, but I loved that she'd smiled at me. She knew I'd stayed out all night in the rain just to catch sight of her."

"Who was she, Dad? Was she the Queen of Tonga?"

"The next day, I found out who my favourite royal was. There were pages and pages in the papers covering the coronation, and among them was a picture of this smiling monarch, beaming from her drenched carriage. The caption said, 'Linger Longer, Queen of Tonga'."

I inspected the photograph in my geography book. I didn't think the picture was of the queen. Queens posed for photos on balconies, with pink handbags, not sitting on the ground accompanied by pigs.

5.
The Abode of Love

The young South African lady at the travel shop appeared at my shoulder.

"Would you like a cup of coffee while you're here? I've just boiled the kettle."

"Oh. Yes, please, milk and one sugar."

I turned back to Ben. "Sorry. I was miles away. The flight goes from London to Los Angeles, then on to Hawaii, then to Tonga, then New Zealand, all on the same ticket?"

"That's right. Air New Zealand have a deal on. As long as you keep travelling west towards New Zealand, you can add several stops for the same price. You must stop in Los Angeles, as that's where the plane refuels. But after that, the Pacific's your oyster."

The coffee arrived.

I took a sip.

I wanted to see the Queen of Tonga.

I wanted her to wave and smile at me, as she had at my father.

"Ben, it sounds perfect. I should go home and discuss this with Fiona. Can I reserve those tickets?"

"I can hold them for 24 hours, but you need to give me a date when you want to leave London. The rest of the flights we can chop and change when you confirm."

"Okay. Fiona's new visa runs out in November. Let's leave London on October 31st. Halloween. I'll remember that date. That'll give us enough time to experience the wonders of Tonga and then have Christmas with her family in New Zealand."

"All right. I'll put a hold on those flights. Here's my card, Simon. Call me when you've had a chat with Fiona."

I stood up and shook his hand. It was like saying goodbye to an old friend.

≈ ≈ ≈

The underground train clickety-clacked from station to station.

"Doors opening. Please mind the gap between the train and the platform. This is Gloucester Road. Change here for the Piccadilly line. This is a District line service to Ealing Broadway. Doors closing."

Come on, come on.

My excitement slowed the train's speed. A second unscheduled halt in a tunnel made me scream inside, my teeth clenched.

I pushed through the doors as soon as the train drew into my station, sprinted home, ran up the stairs to our flat, and smashed open the door. Fiona looked up at me, shocked at my entrance.

"Fiona, we're going to Tonga!"

"We are?"

"It's on the way to New Zealand. I've always wanted to go there, and I've known about it since I was a boy. I'm so excited. Can we book the tickets?"

"Simon, stop. Sit down and tell me all about it. Slowly."

I told her about my meeting with Ben. I told her about my father's reminiscences twenty years ago. I told her about the picture of the lady and the pigs in my schoolbook.

"Tonga?" she asked. "I know lots about Tonga. I studied Tonga in grade twelve."

"You never told me that."

"You never asked. I had no idea you were interested in the place."

"I can't believe we've been together a year and we haven't talked about Tonga. Don't tell me you've been there?"

"No, but I'd love to go. It's the only Pacific island nation the British and the French never colonised, so its culture is pretty unique."

"That settles it. I'll ring Ben and confirm those flights. How long should we stay there?" I asked.

"I reckon, to see the place properly, and get under its skin, you'd need months. The islands are dispersed across hundreds of miles of ocean."

"Mmm okay, not sure our funds will stretch to months."

"Shame. All right, as I remember it has four major island groups. Instead of seeing all of them, let's visit the main one, and choose one other. Let's make friends with the natives, understand the country. Let's be travellers, not tourists. Could we afford six weeks?"

"That sounds good," I said, "I'll lock it in."

I rang Travel Unlimited.

"Ben? Hi, it's Simon. About the flights to New Zealand. Can we reserve them? The ones leaving London on October 31st?"

Ben held the flights. We'd fly from London, stop in Los Angeles long enough to gawp at the plastic playgrounds of Hollywood and Disneyland, fly on to Hawaii for a couple of nights and finally board the plane to Tonga. Six weeks in Tonga.

And after that, a new life in New Zealand with Fiona. I mustn't plan that far ahead yet.

"Fiona, what d'you reckon our chances are of seeing the Queen of Tonga? I mean, it's a tiny country, there's few people, we should be able to find her somewhere."

"You know it's bound to be a different queen to the one your dad exchanged grins with at the coronation? If she was the same one, she'd be about 100 years old by now. Let's go to the library, look her up, and find a travel guide to Tonga while we're there."

≈ ≈ ≈

Tonga, Tonga, Tonga.

As we strolled to the library, Fiona recalled some facts about the nation from her school project.

I marvelled at the word 'Nuku'alofa', the tiny capital city's name, which meant 'The Abode of Love'. I loved the fact the Tongans called island gossip 'The Coconut Wireless'. Fiona informed me there were almost 200 islands in the country, that they grew vanilla, which I hadn't realised was a plant, and that the Tongan word for 'white man' was *palangi,* which she thought meant 'long pig', on account of cannibalism. I wasn't sure about that bit. My idea of a holiday didn't include a stint as dish of the day on a local dinner table.

Fiona also explained that Tonga was a long way off the tourist trail, and we'd be without several home comforts.

At the top of the three steps to the library, a glass door revealed a semi-circular dark wooden desk, with a slim well-dressed man behind it. His old-fashioned suit and haircut belied his youth. The desk contained a computer terminal, and beside him a trolley of books queued for his attention.

We inquired where books about Tonga were, and it felt strangely good that the librarian hadn't heard of it.

He directed me towards the travel section. Meanwhile, Fiona entered the reference room.

The travel shelves had a small selection of books about the Pacific, primarily concerning Australia and New Zealand. There were a few books about Fiji and Tahiti, one about Samoa, and precisely none about Tonga. A book entitled *Guide to the Islands of The Pacific* looked promising. It contained less than one page on Tonga, which told me nothing I didn't already know.

Fiona tugged at my arm. "Come over here. There's something I want to show you, but the book's too heavy to carry."

A huge leather-bound volume lay on a sloping table, open at a page with a sepia picture of a stately lady. She had brown skin with black curly hair, and white robes with fur edging. The caption read: *Queen Sālote Mafile'o Pilolevu, Monarch of the Kingdom of Tonga. 5th April 1918–16th December 1965.*

I stared at a picture of the lady who had entranced my father. Queen Sālote had died before my birth, just twelve years after they'd exchanged grins.

6.
A Letter to the Pacific

I recovered my composure.

"Who's the queen now?"

"Now there's a king, Sālote's son. He's mentioned on the previous page. He's called King Tupou IV. He's married, so there must be a queen. Here she is. Hmm. I'm not sure how to pronounce this. *Ha-la-e-va-lu Ma-ta'a-ho 'A-ho-me'e*. I wonder what they call her for short?"

I didn't care what they called her for short. There was a queen of Tonga. She existed. I'd booked a flight to Tonga, and I was determined to see her.

≈ ≈ ≈

The library had failed to deliver on a travel guide, so I purchased one from a specialist bookshop in central London.

Fiona and I flicked through it, while we ate a bowl of pasta on the couch.

"Let's book our first couple of nights' accommodation," I said, "so we've arranged somewhere to sleep when we get off the plane."

Fiona found the *Where to stay* section.

"It appears the main option is small guest houses and homestays," she said. "No hotels."

"Good. I don't want to stay in some touristy dive, full of obnoxious football-shirt clad idiots, with native dancing shows, and half-price drinks at happy hour. I want to meet some locals, rough it a bit, have the real experience. What d'you reckon?"

"This place sounds okay. *Toni's Guest House and Backpackers*. Let's try him, there's a phone number here."

I rang the number, a string of digits approximately the length of pi.

"Hello? Is that Toni's backpackers in Nuku'alofa?"

A distant voice with a strong northern English accent answered, the words slow and deliberate. This took me by surprise, I had an instant image of a farmer leaning on a gate, wearing a straw hat.

"Well, it was the last time I looked at the sign on the front. Toni speaking, 'ow can I 'elp you?"

"Oh, er, great. My girlfriend and I want to stay for a few weeks, starting in November, do you have any availability?"

"Oh, we can always fit you in. We'll pick you up off the plane. Look for my sign when you walk out of the airport."

"Thanks, Toni. Are we booked?"

"Well, I don't do bookings as such, but you're all right."

I needed to adjust to the way Tonga worked.

"Okay. By the way, which part of Yorkshire are you from?"

"I'm from Lancashire, but never mind."

Oops. Toni's the first person I've spoken to in Tonga, and I've already insulted him.

I turned to Fiona. "That was Toni. We can stay with him, and he'll even collect us from the airport."

"Great! We can spend a lot of time sightseeing in and around the capital. I reckon that'll be your best chance of seeing the queen; that's where the royal palace is. Now, we need to settle on a second island group, and book our internal flights."

Fiona explained the geography of the islands of Tonga, as she read from the guide.

"The main group of islands is known as the Tongatapu group. That's where we'll stay in the capital, Nuku'alofa, when we arrive."

"These Tongan names are ridiculous. I'm sure they just tip a tin of alphabet spaghetti on a plate, and pick a few letters out."

Fiona ignored me and continued reading.

"Then there's three other groups. The most remote and hard to reach are the Niuas. They're tiny, and flights are irregular. It says here there's no real schedule; the plane leaves when there's enough people booked to justify taking off."

I'd never heard of an airline that flew on this basis. The different way of working in Tonga surprised me.

"The Niuas sound tempting," I said, "I've always wanted to stay on a proper desert island. But we can't get stuck there with no plane, and miss our international flight on to New Zealand."

"Good point. They're probably just a bit too remote. Vava'u is the next group of islands. It says the people are more used to tourists, as it's one of the cruising capitals of the world. Between August and November, it's jam packed with hundreds of yachts."

"That doesn't sound attractive at all," I said, "I don't think we'd experience the real Tonga, if we were staying in the South Seas equivalent of Monaco."

Fiona laughed. "I'm sure it'll be nothing like Monaco. The last group of islands is Ha'apai. It's the closest to Tongatapu. Wow. Listen to this: The isolation of the Ha'apai Group will astound you. Coral reefs, beaches and lagoons straight out of travel advertisements, the friendliest people, and a place where tourists are almost unheard of. Ha'apai life has barely changed in over a century."

"Go on, it sounds perfect."

"The Ha'apai Islands are only a 30-minute flight from Nuku'alofa, but are pretty much unvisited. Although flights are frequent, the plane from Nuku'alofa to Vava'u will fly right over Ha'apai without stopping, unless you reconfirm with the airline you want to disembark there."

"We'd better make sure we do that."

"Divers especially love Ha'apai, because of the pristine untouched underwater world."

This was a bonus. I'd been scuba diving on previous holidays, and passed my rescue diver qualification. I'd love to experience it in a proper tropical location. Fiona wasn't so sure it was her thing, but she wanted to try snorkelling.

"Fiona, I'm sold, I want to visit the Ha'apai Islands. Does the guide mention any places to stay? I don't think we should make any firm bookings in Ha'apai. Let's leave it until we get there."

"That's not like you; you plan everything." Fiona made fun of me.

It's true though. Maybe I'm learning the Tongan way.

"I'm looking for the accommodation section," she said, "hang on a tic. The town of Pangai's the big smoke in the Ha'apai

Islands, but when I say 'big smoke', the population's only about 2000. There's a place listed here called 'The Bounty Resort'. You'd be interested in this. It's a desert island with no facilities at all, not even electricity or running water. You need your own tent and camping equipment, and food, there are no shops or anything. You might be the only people on the island."

"Wow. Real Robinson Crusoe stuff. Can we stay there? That'd be an extraordinary experience."

"You can't book it, there's no phone or fax number. There's an address. Why don't we write to them, to make sure they're still taking guests?"

"Write to them?" I said. "How quaint. I can't remember the last time I wrote a letter to anyone."

We handwrote a letter and posted it.

'Mr. Kapo Folau,
The Bounty Resort,
Pangai,
The Ha'apai Islands,
Kingdom of Tonga.

Dear Mr Folau,

We are coming to stay in Tonga in November, and would like to camp on your island. Please could you confirm you are accepting guests, and you can take us by boat from Pangai? Also please tell us the essentials that we would need to bring.

Regards
Simon and Fiona,
London, England.'

"I bet we don't receive a reply," I said.

7.
Half an Aeroplane

How could I survive another six months at work? Tonga filled my mind every waking moment. I arranged a medical appointment as an excuse to slip out of the office early and run a few errands. There was a lot to organise.

Ben recognised me when I sat down at his desk.

"Hello," he said, "how are your plans going?"

"Great, thanks. We've been looking at places to stay in Tonga. The accommodation seems to be backpackers and homestays, which is fine with us."

"I think there's a hotel," said Ben, "I seem to remember it's called The International Pacific. I'll find out how much it costs."

"Ben, it's okay. We don't want to stay in a hotel, thanks anyway. I need to book some internal flights though. We want to visit some islands called The Ha'apai Group."

"All right. Only one carrier flies domestic routes in Tonga, they're called Friendly Island Airways. I'll see what options they offer."

What an amazing name. Friendly Island Airways.

I gazed around the shop as Ben clicked his mouse. Enormous maps served as wallpaper, and a giant photo of a girl in hot pants caught my eye. She hung upside down from a high bridge under the heading *New Zealand.*

Ben finished clicking. "Here we go. They changed their name to Royal Tongan Airlines. They own five propeller planes flying between the islands, and half a Boeing jet that flies to New Zealand and back."

"Half a Boeing jet? How can you have half a jet?"

"I've seen that plane before, in Auckland," Ben said, "it's part owned by Royal Tongan Airlines, and part owned by Air Pacific, the Fijian airline. It says Royal Tongan Airlines on one side, and Air Pacific on the other, with the different airlines' logos on each side of the tail. Things work a bit differently in the Pacific."

The more I delved into life in Tonga; the more I found out how differently.

"How long did you want to stay in Nuku'alofa before you fly to Ha'apai?" asked Ben.

"Well, we've booked about six weeks in Tonga," I said. "Let's spend a few weeks in Nuku'alofa, maybe ten days in the Ha'apai Islands, and back to Nuku'alofa for our flight to New Zealand. That means we'd fly to Ha'apai around the beginning of December. Will that work?"

Ben concentrated as his fingers flew across the keyboard faster than a maestro playing Rachmaninov. I crossed and uncrossed my legs in impatience. With a final mouse click, he turned the screen round and faced it towards me. The display showed an incomprehensible computer diarrhoea of bright green numbers and letters on a black background.

Ben translated. "Royal Tongan fly to Vav'au every day, and stop in the Ha'apai Islands en-route, apart from Sundays, when no planes fly anywhere at all in Tonga. What about flying there on Saturday 7th December, and flying back on Monday 16th? That'd give you enough time back in Nuku'alofa, before your flight to New Zealand."

"Sounds great. Let's book it."

"All right. You'll take off from Nuku'alofa, and land at Lifuka Island Airport in the Ha'apai Islands about half an hour later. Hmmm. There's a note here on the system. It says you must go to the Royal Tongan Airlines office a couple of days in advance to reconfirm you want to disembark in Ha'apai, otherwise the plane might carry straight on to Va'vau without stopping."

"Yep, Fiona's already warned me about this. It's amazing to think an airline works on such an informal basis."

Ben laughed. "I've travelled a lot in third-world countries. You'll find plenty of things work on an informal basis."

Ben furrowed his brow and looked at me. He pushed his spectacles back into his hair, where they joined another pair ensnared well beyond extrication.

"You're ending the flight in New Zealand, aren't you?"

"Yes, we're going to live there, for a while at least."

"You'll need a visa. As a tourist they'll only let you stay six months, and they'll want to see a return ticket. You might be able to apply for a de-facto relationship visa. There's one in my passport because of my Kiwi girlfriend. How long have you and Fiona been living together?"

"She's been my girlfriend for a year, but we only started flatting a few weeks ago."

"Hmm, that won't be long enough for a partner visa. I'm sure they'll give you a working holiday permit at first. They last twelve months, and you could apply for the partner one after that. Maybe drop into New Zealand House and ask them? It's at the bottom of Haymarket, near Trafalgar Square."

Ben's proving to be invaluable.

"I can visit there now, on the way home. Thanks, Ben. Do I need any other visas for anywhere else?"

"No, the USA and Tonga allow tourists to enter for up to three months, you only need the New Zealand one. Oh, I almost forgot, when you go to New Zealand House, take your passport with you. They'll need to hang on to it for around a week. I speak from experience."

"Luckily, I've got it with me. I thought you might need to see it."

≈ ≈ ≈

The grey concrete of New Zealand House matched the colour of the London sky as I entered the lobby, the tiled floor framed by giant paintings of impossibly stunning scenery. Enormous pots containing tall ferns flanked glass cabinets displaying Maori artefacts. I approached a white plastic sign standing at the lift, which invited me to ascend to the third floor in the event I required the immigration department.

The doors opened onto a large waiting area, full of different nationalities and cultures. Two immigration officers served customers, and I tore off ticket number 172. The display advertised number 159; I prepared for a long wait.

A pile of promotional brochures on a low table helped relieve the waiting-room boredom. A grass-skirted tattooed brown man with a spear stared from the front cover, his tongue sticking out, looking directly into the camera.

He resembled the man in my schoolbook. I recalled the original inhabitants of New Zealand were Polynesians, the same race as the Tongans.

45 minutes after I had arrived, it was my turn. I sat down at the young lady's desk. She had a pleasant brown bob and freckles.

"How can I help you today?"

Her accent's the same as Fiona's.

"I want to apply for a working holiday visa please."

"Okay, to be eligible for one of them you must be between 18 and 30, with no dependent children."

I allowed I was in the age range, and that I had no dependent children to my knowledge. She smiled. She'd heard that joke a thousand times.

"We only issue 500 of these visas per year, and as it's halfway through May, we might have run out. Let me check."

I suffered an anxious wait while she disappeared into a back office. The ticket numbers continued creeping up.

"You're in luck. 34 left." She smiled at my relief. "Could you please take this form, and fill it in? Do you have your passport with you?"

"I do, would you like it?"

"Not immediately. You can either fill in the form now, and bring it back to me, or you can return another day. You need to leave your passport with us for a week, and we'll stick the visa in it for you. Oh, and the fee is £120."

"I'll fill it in now, thanks," I said. "I don't want to come back tomorrow and find out you've sold the last 34 visas."

"That's unlikely, but best to be safe I suppose."

The unnecessarily elongated document took a long time to complete. I gave it back to her together with my passport and credit card, glad to have another item ticked off.

≈ ≈ ≈

Doctor Atkins sat behind his antique desk in a leather swivel chair, his wrinkled hands rested on the arms. Books lined the walls of his front room, where he kept a surgery for his remaining patients. He finished writing with a fountain pen, before he dabbed his notes with blotting paper and looked up at me over half-rimmed spectacles.

"Simon, isn't it?"

He removed the glasses, letting them dangle from a gold chain around his neck.

"How's your father keeping?" he asked, "I haven't seen him in a while."

"He's very well, thank you, Doctor, enjoying his retirement."

"As am I, Simon, as am I. Surgery only two afternoons a week now, to stop me from going senile. Anyway, what can I do for you today?"

"I'm travelling to Tonga with my girlfriend, and I wanted to find out if you recommend having any injections."

"Let me have a look."

Doctor Atkins pulled a slim volume out of a desk drawer, replaced his spectacles on his nose, and flicked through the pages. He paused near the end.

"Togo? Western Africa. Yes, you need: typhoid, cholera, yellow fever, rabies, meningitis, polio, measles…."

I stopped him in the middle of his shopping list of illnesses, and spoke a bit louder.

"Not Togo – Tonga," I said. "It's a South Pacific island."

"Ah, Tonga. I remember, the coronation. Linger Longer, Queen of Tonga."

"Yes, that's why we're going. I'm hoping to catch a glimpse of her successor."

He returned to his list of countries and their assorted ailments, then looked up.

"Not mentioned. No injections needed. You're off the hook. Anything else I can help you with?"

"That's all. Thanks, Doctor, I appreciate it."

"Nice to see you Simon. Please give my regards to your dad."

"I will, goodbye."

I hurried home to Fiona. On the way I noticed a sandwich board, close to our local park, advertising *Fletcher's Steam Fair—coming this weekend. Casual staff wanted.* I thought nothing of it.

≈ ≈ ≈

"Hi, Fiona, are you okay?"

"It's so boring being stuck in the flat watching every available program on daytime TV. I can't have a job on this stupid tourist visa, and I can't go anywhere or do anything, as we're saving money for travelling."

"I promise it'll be worth it. Let's walk through the park to the river before dinner. That doesn't cost any money, and we can chat about our plans."

Across a busy road, the peace of Ravenscourt Park formed an oasis of nature within the unforgiving concrete of West London. By walking through it from end to end, we could reach the liquid sanctuary of the River Thames.

Fiona's tight grip on my hand reassured me her mood was improving.

"I'm sorry to be grumpy," she said. "I'm all alone during the day while you're at work. I'm so excited about our trip, and it's still months away."

"Let me tell you what I've done today," I said. "I went to see Ben."

"You did? That's a bit of a trek from your work."

"I know, I skived off for the afternoon. Anyway, he's booked us the internal flights to the Ha'apai Islands. He warned me again about making sure we tell the airline we want to disembark there. Then I had an appointment with Doctor Atkins, and we don't need any injections for Tonga."

"Thank goodness for that. I hate needles. Was the Ha'apai flight expensive?"

"It was rather. Only one airline flies that route, so there's no competition."

"This is eating into our travel funds a lot," said Fiona. "We'll have no money to spend once we're there."

"I know. We've got to save a bit harder over the next few months."

Fiona looked uncertain. "The cost of Los Angeles and Hawaii hotels, and food every day, and we want to do some sightseeing as well, it's so much. And that's all before we arrive in Tonga. I'm not sure we've saved enough money to do this."

"It'll be all right, we're good at budgeting. Oh, and something else. Ben told me I need a New Zealand visa, so I dropped into the embassy today, and filled in the form. It lasts a year, and they charged me £120."

Oops. I shouldn't have told her how much it cost.

"£120? This is adding up, isn't it?" Fiona became quiet as we walked.

The noise of engines and the shouts of men at work intruded on the peace. Large lorries parked on the lawns, and tarpaulins the size of deflated hot air balloons lay beside the herbaceous borders.

We walked towards the action.

"It's a fairground." Fiona said, "an old-fashioned Victorian one."

She hurried me towards an area where groups of men were erecting a merry-go-round and huge swings. We observed them from a distance.

'Fletcher's Steam Fair." Fiona read from the side of a vintage lorry.

This triggered a recent memory. "There was a sign advertising it on the way back home from the Doctor's," I said. "It also said they wanted casual staff."

"What are we waiting for?" Fiona strode off towards the hubbub.

"Hang on." I grabbed her arm. "You're not allowed to work on your tourist visa."

8.
The Overboats

"Never mind my visa, Simon. Do you want money for travelling or not?"

Fiona marched towards a vintage caravan. A middle-aged man leant against it with one hand. Brown braces were attached to his workmen's trousers and cascaded over his ample stomach, visible between missing buttons on his open-necked shirt. His demeanour suggested he was The Management.

"Hello," said Fiona, "we saw your sign saying you need casual staff. We live around the corner, and we can work this weekend. In fact, I can work any time."

"Hmph."

He looked us up and down over his ZZ Top beard.

"Talk to Troy. He's the dark-haired chap over there, painting the side of that lorry."

He turned away to speak to one of his workers, and it was clear the conversation was over.

Fiona kept her voice down. "He didn't seem friendly."

"Well, you know these carnival types, they keep themselves to themselves, they don't like outsiders."

We approached Troy.

"Stop," I said. I pulled Fiona back. "I want to watch him paint."

Beautiful cursive script appeared on the ancient lorry, as we watched Troy hand-paint delicate letters, using a small brush and a tiny tin pot.

This man was a genuine artist. Watching his meticulous movements relaxed me.

"Come on, Simon." Fiona tugged my arm.

"Troy?" she asked.

The man put down his paint tin, and turned, smiling. His unruly black hair and dark skin complemented his working man attire.

"Hello, yes, I'm Troy. What can I do for you?"

"I'm Fiona, and this is my boyfriend Simon. Your sign said you need casual staff? We live around the corner, and we're looking for some extra money for the summer. Do you have anything we could help with?"

"I'm sure we can find something. Are you free to work this weekend?"

"Yes, both days."

"The fair runs from 2 p.m. to 10 p.m. I can pay you for eight hours each day. It's £4 an hour, cash. We trust you to sort out your own income tax." He winked.

"Sounds perfect," said Fiona. "What do you need us to do?"

"Well, I need someone to take the money on the kids' swings. Could you do that, Fiona? And, Simon, is it? You could work the overboats." He pointed at another man nearby. "Stuart here will show you how they work."

"Great!" said Fiona, "we'll be here on Saturday. Oh, who's the man with the beard and braces? I'm not sure he likes us."

Troy laughed. "That's my dad, Bob Fletcher. He's a bit gruff, but once you're part of the team, you'll find everyone respects him. My mum and my two brothers work here as well. If you turn up at 1 p.m. we'll kit you out before the fair opens. See you then."

Troy returned to his painting, and we continued our evening stroll towards the river.

"Isn't that fantastic?" Fiona said, "that gives us an extra £128 between us this weekend, and because we're working, we won't have time to spend it."

"I hope there's more work after this weekend," I said. "£128 by itself won't go far, it'll only cover the cost of my New Zealand visa. I wonder what 'overboats' are?"

≈ ≈ ≈

Fairground workers rushed across the site carrying ladders, tools, and money bags. Sideshows displayed more stuffed animals than Prince Philip's living room. Flashing lights advertised dodgems and flying cars. In the centre stood the huge merry-go-round, with meticulously painted horses poised to gallop.

We reported for work, and Troy explained how the fair worked and when he'd pay us. He introduced me to Stuart, who wasn't a Fletcher family member, but he'd lived and travelled with them his whole life.

Stuart's curly blond hair blew in the breeze as he inducted me in overboat operation.

"This ride is the oldest working fairground ride in the world," he said. "Various showmen have displayed it since 1872."

He pointed out the date painted on the front, as reverentially as if he'd been exhibiting a Rembrandt.

I inspected the overboats. Two wooden rowing skiffs were attached to a small octagonal ferris wheel. Each contained double seats. Victorian nautical scenes decorated their sides. One boat was at the apex of the wheel, high in the air. The second sat at the bottom, exactly opposite.

"How do they turn?" I asked, looking for an engine.

"You turn them with this handle." Stuart indicated a metal lever, similar to a crank on the front of a vintage car. He paused to observe my reaction. I wasn't the first person to whom he'd given this explanation.

"I turn them myself? Troy didn't mention I needed to be an Olympic weightlifter for this job."

"Ah-haaa," said Stuart, "it's all a question of balance. Let me show you."

He picked up a huge black iron weight, a larger version of those my grandmother had used to measure cooking ingredients. It said '20 lbs' on the side, in raised black embossing,

"Imagine this weight is a small child. If I place it in the bottom boat, and turn the handle so the boat with the weight is at the top, what's going to happen?"

"Well," I said, "seeing as the boat at the top is now heavier by 20 lbs, I presume it would fall down the other side of the Ferris wheel?"

"Exactly. You catch on quick."

This is exciting, I've taken my first step to becoming a fairground worker.

Stuart resumed my education.

"How d'you think we'd prevent the top boat plummeting down again?"

"We could put another weight in the bottom boat. That'd balance them."

"Correct. Make sure the weight of children in the top is equal to those in the bottom, and use these weights to balance them. If the weight in each boat is identical, you can turn the ride with your little finger."

"But how do I estimate how much each child weighs?" I asked, over-complicating the process.

Stuart laughed. "You'll work it out." He handed me a bag full of change to tie round my waist. "Fair opens in fifteen minutes." My overboat operator's diploma was complete.

I hoped the ride wasn't too popular, at least until I'd had some practice.

Meanwhile, on the adjacent attraction, Fiona had an easier job. A tall A-frame held eight double-ended swing boats in a long line. Each could seat two children, and they were all decorated with Troy's beautiful artwork. Ropes hung from the frame. Once the children pulled the ropes, the swings started moving. The harder they pulled; the higher they swung.

"How's your training going?" I asked her.

"Great, all I have to do is take the money, and if there's a queue, make sure no-one hogs the swings too long." She sported an identical money bag around her waist.

"Sounds easy. I need a maths qualification for my ride."

"I'm sure you'll work it out," she said, echoing Stuart's words.

Next to Fiona were the 'big striker' and the 'little striker'. These were sideshows, the bigger one for adults; the smaller one for children. After paying their money, the player collected an age-appropriate mallet.

The player smacked the mallet against a big round button, as hard as possible. A metal striker ran up a tall pole. The harder you hit; the higher it flew up.

Stronger players could make it hit the bell at the top, more drunken ones showing off to their admiring girlfriends often missed the button altogether.

Ian ran the strikers. Like us, he was a casual employee. He'd been working with the Fletchers every weekend since he was a teenager.

"Don't you worry about Bob Fletcher," he said, "he's a pussy cat. He just wants to make sure everyone's working hard, and doing their job. As long as you're reliable, and don't mess him around, he'll be fine. And remember it's casual work, there's no sick pay or holidays or anything. But if the fair's busy and they do well, they give us weekend workers a bit of a bonus."

I liked the sound of that.

"So," asked Ian, "How come you two ended up working with this mob?"

"We're saving to go travelling. We're off for six weeks to Tonga."

"Tonga? Never heard of it. I go to Benidorm for my holidays. Same hotel every year. We love it there, me and the wife. Good British food, none of that foreign stuff, and everyone speaks English. The manager knows us by name now."

Two small customers waited for a ride in the overboats, and I left him to his reminiscing. Benidorm sounded as enticing as a week in a launderette.

≈ ≈ ≈

A chattering queue of small children for both the overboats and the swings demanded our attention well into Sunday evening, but after dark, most of the young families had left. Our feet ached after eight hours of standing, and my arms and shoulders burned as if I'd been in a push-up contest with Arnold Schwarzenegger. My balancing calculations weren't quite right yet.

At 10 o'clock the sky exploded with fireworks, in a display designed to keep the public at the fairground spending their money until the last minute. We approached Troy's caravan, and he handed us our salaries in bags of pound coins.

"There's a bit extra for each of you. You did well, thank you. Next weekend's a bank holiday Monday. There's three days' work if you want it."

"Fantastic!" said Fiona, "of course we do."

How's my body going to survive?

9.
I Quit

Our work at Fletcher's Steam Fair left me in agony at the end of every weekend, but we kept it up for the entire summer. Saturday and Sunday saw us heading off on the Underground train to the fair's new location, crossing London to unfamiliar suburbs. Before the fair opened, we saw the results of the men's work during the week, breaking the fair down on its old site, packing it on to the ancient lorries, transporting it at a highway-clogging pace of fifteen miles per hour, and rebuilding it to become a children's magical Victorian wonderland by the following Saturday.

We came to know the Fletcher family and their regular employees well. Bob Fletcher and his family had been in the fairground business all their lives. They'd begun by restoring and showing the 100-year-old merry-go-round or 'gallopers'.

I made the mistake on my first weekend of calling it a carousel.

Troy told me off. "Don't let Dad hear you say that word. Carousel is an American term, and they rotate the other way. We always call ours a merry-go-round."

The merry-go-round played complicated invigorating Wurlitzer-style music from its steam organ, Troy standing at the engine, his boilersuit and face sooty black as a train driver's. It particularly impressed me this travelling family ensured the first tune every Sunday was 'Abide with me.'

As we journeyed home late at night after our fair shifts, we sat next to each other, the only sober people on the train. The happy party people laughed, hugged, and snogged. I contemplated them with the envy of the seven-day-a-week worker.

"It's all good," said Fiona, "think of the travelling money we're earning."

As September came to an end, the fair closed for the winter and there was no more work for us. Through working the summer weekends and public holidays, we'd saved over £2000.

≈ ≈ ≈

"D'you realise, it's only a month until we leave England?" said Fiona. "I'm really going to miss London. There's a heap of things I haven't seen here yet."

"I hope it's not an expensive heap. We don't want to spend all our travelling money before we leave. I'm still not convinced we've saved enough."

"Most of my list is quite cheap," she said. "Some of it's free, such as art galleries, museums, parks. And like your infatuation with the Queen of Tonga, I want to visit Princess Diana's house, and try to catch a glimpse of her before I leave England. All I'd need is a travel card."

"I've thought of something," I said. "You mentioned we leave in a month. I haven't handed in my notice at work."

"Wow, did you forget about that?"

Fiona's eyes formed slits, and she pursed her lips to one side. "What date is your salary paid on?"

"The last Friday in the month, which in October is the 25th."

"And we fly out on the 31st. Don't tell them you're leaving until you get paid. If you break the news to them now, they might not pay you for the last month."

"I can't give them only six days' notice," I said.

"Check your employment contract. A month is normal, but it's not always the case."

I found the paperwork in the filing cabinet, and glossed over the legalese, which read like the transcript of a parliamentary debate.

"Here," I thrust it at Fiona, "you have a look. It doesn't seem to mention a notice period at all."

Fiona read it through and confirmed it didn't. "Hand in your resignation after your pay goes in. They can hardly sack you."

She was right. It didn't matter, I wasn't very keen on my job anyway.

Meanwhile, when she wasn't taking her day trips to say goodbye to the sights of London, and track down the elusive Princess Diana, Fiona stayed at home, and packed up our lives as we prepared to leave England.

≈ ≈ ≈

I returned one day to find Fiona on the floor, surrounded by bags.

"I've weighed the luggage," she said, "it's 80 kilos with all the camping gear. That's a lot to be lugging round the world. Let's take some of it out. We won't need winter clothes and jackets, America and Tonga are going to be hot. And what about all your dive gear?"

The dive gear was as heavy as a headbanger's record collection, and it occupied an entire bag. A friend who'd used it once, and lost interest, had sold it to me, and I couldn't wait to try it out in tropical waters.

"I can't leave the dive gear behind. We're going to have to send another box directly to New Zealand."

We were already shipping three boxes via sea, possessions Fiona had collected during her two years in England, and I was shipping my guitar. If I couldn't find any employment in New Zealand, my terrible guitar playing might appeal to drunken pub-going Kiwis. It certainly wouldn't interest sober ones.

"Can we cram some more clothes into the boxes we're sending?" I asked. "Shipping another box will cost £100 which we can't spare."

"I know, let's wrap your guitar in these winter jackets. That'll protect them more than the bubble-wrap, and they won't cost any more to send."

We took the guitar out, and squished our fluffy coats around it. I burst the bubble-wrap absent-mindedly, making a sound like a pensioner trying to hold in flatulence.

"Oh, and Mike and Sarah can look after the flat for us," said Fiona. "They'll pay enough to cover the mortgage and the bills. We won't have to worry about anything.

"That's great, it saves us having to find tenants."

I looked at Fiona. "I can't wait to travel with you," I said. "This is all getting real. I'm quite nervous."

"I know. It's exciting and a little frightening."

≈ ≈ ≈

Keeping the secret of my impending departure from my colleagues was as difficult as touching my elbow with my tongue. In meetings

I had to stop myself from saying, "Why should I care? I'll be lying on a beach in the Pacific by then."

My resignation speech played out repeatedly in my head, as the underground train travelled into the city. The boss wasn't going to react well to six days' notice.

Martin was already in his office. I stuck my head round the door.

"Any chance of a quick word?" I said.

Martin looked up at me, preoccupied. His suit jacket was in disarray on the back of his chair, and his tie hung loosely, the top button of his shirt undone.

Has he been at work all night?

"Of course," he said.

This was it. Time to deliver the news.

"Martin, I wanted to advise you I'm going to be leaving the company. I'm travelling overseas with my girlfriend and we fly out next week. I'm sorry not to be giving you much notice, but I checked my employment contract and…."

Martin held up his hand. I paused in mid-resignation.

"Simon, I want you to pretend you didn't just say any of that. Go back to your desk. I'll discuss it with you this afternoon."

"But…."

"Just give me a few hours."

This was more mysterious than an episode of Scooby Doo.

Was he telling me I couldn't resign? Why hadn't he let me finish what I was saying?

I returned to my desk, and couldn't concentrate on any work. Instead, I made a list of instructions for whoever took on my job, which kept me occupied for the morning. Lunchtime came and went. I tidied my filing cabinet. I repeatedly looked over at Martin's office, hoping he'd invite me to come in. But his glass door was closed, and his phone never left his ear.

At three o'clock in the afternoon, Martin's door opened, and he stood looking around the office. I tried to catch his eye, but he looked past me at my colleague, Helen. He called her in, shutting the door behind her, and through the glass wall I could see they were having a serious conversation. A few minutes later, his door reopened, and Helen marched to her desk, tears running down her cheeks.

What's going on?

Martin reappeared in the doorway, and beckoned another of my co-workers, Robin, an older man who wasn't far off retirement. Again, the door closed, and a serious conversation was visible. Robin left Martin's office a short while later. He looked happier than I had ever seen him.

This is all very odd.

Martin stood once again in his doorway. "Simon, could you please join me?"

I walked over to his office. He shut the door and invited me to take a seat. Before he could sit down, I started talking.

"Martin, about this morning, I…."

"Simon." He stopped me mid-sentence. "I have some very bad news for you."

10.
A Lucky Lad

Martin's face displayed a serious expression, but his eyes had the faintest smile in them. He picked up a piece of paper from a pile in front of him, and referred to it as he spoke.

"Simon, the company's been sold, and as a result there are going to be some redundancies. I'm afraid to say your job is among them, and the upshot of this is we don't have any employment for you from now on."

What? This is extraordinary. Why hasn't anyone told us before?

I sat in stunned silence. Martin continued.

"You will, of course receive a redundancy payment. Taking into consideration the four years you've worked for us, this will be six months' salary. Your last day will be the 30th November..." his face formed a wry smile, "… although based on our conversation this morning, I quite understand if you want to leave sooner."

What a manager. Rather than accept my resignation, he'd delayed me until he could announce the sale of the business to everyone, leaving me six months' money better off.

"Wow. Martin, thank you so much. You've been the best boss ever."

"No problem, Simon. Have a wonderful time overseas, and please contact me if you need a reference."

He stood up to shake my hand. "You can leave today if you want. Give your pass and any other company property to the office manager. I expect you may have some packing to do."

"Thanks, Martin. I need to make one phone call before I go."

The joy inside me threatened to explode over my face as I walked back to my desk. Helen was talking on the phone, terribly upset, and I remembered redundancy wasn't a positive experience for everyone. I couldn't keep my excitement to myself, so I approached Robin, who was busy boxing up his possessions.

"Hi Robin, have you had the news too?"

"It's fantastic, Simon. I was going to retire at Christmas, anyway. They're sending me off with over a year's money. I can afford to book the Mediterranean cruise my wife's always wanted to take. But what about you? You seem happier than you ought to be, for someone who just lost their job."

"I'm emigrating to New Zealand, Robin. I was about to hand in my notice to Martin when he told me. This is great, that's six months extra money I wasn't banking on."

"New Zealand, did you say?"

Robin sat down, took off his glasses, and ran his hand back through his remaining hair. He looked up at me.

"You're a lucky lad. Take this opportunity and make the most of it, young Simon. I had the chance to emigrate to New Zealand in my twenties, but I was never brave enough to go, and I've regretted that decision all my life. You'll love it."

"Thanks, Robin, it's been good working with you. Enjoy your retirement."

I left him packing up pictures of his grandchildren, and returned to my desk. I rang my girlfriend.

"Hi Fiona, put on your best dress and come into town. I'm taking you out."

"It's a bit difficult for me to put on my best dress, it's at the bottom of one of the shipping boxes. Why, what's happened? You can't have won the lottery; you don't buy the tickets."

"Meet me dressed as you are then. I've got some amazing news."

"All right, mystery man. I'll find you outside your work. Give me an hour."

Five o'clock took longer to come than it had any other day of my life.

I stepped out of my office building for the last time ever. Fiona ran up to me.

"What do you need to tell me? Why couldn't you say it over the phone? You sounded so excited."

"Would you like to have dinner? How about My Old Dutch pancake house? We haven't been there for ages."

"Gosh, yes, I'd love to, but we can't afford it, can we?"

"Trust me."

Hanging baskets of flowers dangled either side of the blue-and-white door, as we stepped out of the cold. The familiar warm smell of pancake ingredients filled the restaurant, and noisy pre-theatre diners chattered. The waiter seated us near the kitchens, dropped two menus in front of us, and left to attend to adjacent customers.

"Come on, spill the beans. Why are we here?" asked Fiona.

"You know how we've been saving hard, and working at Fletcher's fair, and we're still worried we haven't got enough spending money?"

"Yes, I'm pretty sure we haven't."

"And you know how I was giving notice at work today?"

"Yes, yes, go on, please tell me, what's happened?"

"They've made me redundant."

"What?"

"I entered Martin's office to say I was resigning, and he told me my job was redundant."

"Is that a good thing?"

"It is when it comes with six months tax-free salary."

"Wow, are you for real?"

"Yep, it's paid into my account as a lump sum next week."

"Oh my goodness," she said, "that's fantastic. Now we can really enjoy ourselves travelling and still have some money remaining, so we won't have to impose on my parents. I've been a bit concerned; I don't think getting a job in New Zealand will be as easy as it has been in London."

"Don't worry about that now. Champagne, dear?"

"I agree, let's celebrate. Which one's the drinks menu?"

≈ ≈ ≈

The foreign exchange clerk at the bank regarded us strangely as we unloaded our hard-earned fairground money on to her counter. We'd counted it all into the correct little clear plastic bags, 43 of them with 50 one-pound coins in each.

She placed them on a weighing machine one by one.

"£2,150. Which currency would you like these in?" she asked.

"Could we please have five hundred US dollars, and the rest in Tongan?"

"Tongan? Mmm, not sure, let me look."

She studied her screen, clicking her mouse.

"Sorry, we don't carry Tongan. Would you still like me to give you the US dollars?"

"Yes please. Do you have any idea where we can find Tongan money?"

"There's a specialist money exchange on Oxford Street. 'Currency World' or something. They might have it. Sorry."

We walked round the corner to the money exchange. It was the same story. No Tongan money. The man informed us the Tongan currency was the *pa'anga*, and it was about two to the pound, but he didn't have any.

"Now what are we going to do?" asked Fiona.

"Maybe we could ask Ben? He knows everything to do with travel. He helped me with my visa as well."

"Sure, I'm intrigued to meet this guru you've been dealing with."

Ben was in his usual position behind his desk, tapping at his computer, his headset competing with several pairs of glasses lost in his hair.

"Hello, Simon. And you must be Fiona. It's not long until you fly out is it? What can I do for you?"

"I know this isn't part of your service, but we're a bit stuck. We can't find Tongan currency. Do you know where we could exchange our pounds for some?"

"I think you'll have to take some US dollar travellers cheques, and change them when you arrive in Nuku'alofa. Another client of mine had to do that. The money isn't available outside Tonga."

There was the answer. We said goodbye to Ben, and went to another branch of our bank to buy some travellers cheques.

Back at our apartment a letter lay in the communal mailbox with our names on it. It had an unusual stamp, postmarked two months previously. The perfect cursive handwriting reminded me of the Christmas cards I received from my grandfather.

I couldn't think who it would be from.

11. Unemployed, Homeless and Vagrant

The envelope crinkled as I turned it over and pulled it open, scanning the contents impatiently.

"What's that, Simon?"

I read it aloud to Fiona.

"Pangai, Lifuka Island.

Ha'apai Islands,

Kingdom of Tonga.

Dear Simon and Fiona,

You may certainly stay at my Bounty Resort. I can give you a ride on my fishing boat. Come and ask for me at the wharf in Pangai. Everyone knows me. Bring a tent and everything you need. There is nothing on the island, except drinking water which comes from the well.

Yours sincerely,

Kapo Folau."

I grinned at Fiona.

"We're going to stay on a real desert island. Castaways."

"Robinson Crusoe and Girl Friday."

"Don't forget Friday did everything for Crusoe. I can't wait, lying on the beach, while you cook dinner after giving me a massage. OW, that hurt."

"I think, Simon, we can take turns at being Crusoe."

I carefully folded the letter back into the envelope, and put it with the rest of our travel documents.

≈ ≈ ≈

Pumpkins and plastic spiders decorated houses in our street. Little ghosts, vampires, witches, and one recycled Superman swarmed in the darkness from door to door. Rockets and crackers sounded in the distance, as rehearsals for Guy Fawkes night helped London's residents enjoy an authentic re-enactment of life during a World War II bombing raid.

Our minds weren't focussed on vampires, nor on gunpowder, treason, and plot. We walked to the underground station staggering under the weight of 80 kilos of luggage, strapped on our backs and carried in our hands. It occurred to me that in the last week I'd given up my pass for my work, and the keys to our flat. This new experience of being unemployed, homeless, and vagrant was surprisingly liberating.

Fiona and I sat in silence on the train, each of us thinking about this massive pivot in our lives, and wondering what the future would bring.

The bulkiness of our baggage made me so grateful to the fellow passenger who held the train doors for us at Heathrow Airport, and gave us a fighting chance of retrieving it all before the train disappeared with Fiona's vital cargo of bikinis and summer dresses.

I approached the ticket office window.

"Could I hand in my travel card for a full refund please?" I asked.

This request puzzled the ticket office man.

"Don't you need this any longer?"

"I'm emigrating to New Zealand, so I don't."

He regarded me sadly as he handed me my money.

"Please take me with you…."

≈ ≈ ≈

Accents similar to Fiona's filled the cabin with chatter, as we took our places in the centre aisle of the Air New Zealand plane. The couple in the adjacent seats turned out to be neighbours of Fiona's Aunt.

"This always happens," said Fiona. "We call the South Island, 'The Village', everyone knows someone who knows someone."

At 8 p.m. the plane was wheels up for Los Angeles, and for the first time I was leaving England with no idea when I would return.

Fiona grabbed my arm. "This is so exciting. I can't believe I'm taking my own Englishman home with me."

I can't believe I'm going.

"Anyway," I said, "before that, we're going to experience the wonders of Tonga."

I sat back in my seat, and stared up at the curly fern shadow design drawn on the plane ceiling.

Tonga.

The Abode of Love.

Linger Longer Queen of Tonga.

I'm on my way to find you.

≈ ≈ ≈

A light midnight breeze cooled us outside arrivals at LAX and I tied my jumper around my waist, as we hefted our 1000 tonnes of luggage along the pavement, searching the illuminated signs for the correct stop to catch our hotel's shuttle bus.

"The sign says Hotel Transfers, but I can't work out where the arrow's pointing," said Fiona. "What's the name of our hotel again?"

"Comfort Inn. Oh no, there it goes."

A bus with 'Comfort Inn' illuminated on the front flew past, devoid of passengers.

"Where did it come from?" she asked. "We'll have to wait for the next one."

"The other hotel buses seem to be over there."

A few people were standing at a stop a short distance away. We dragged our bags across the road and waited, studying the front of each bus as it turned the corner and approached. Comfort Inn wasn't one of the destinations advertised.

"We don't have to call them to collect us, do we?" Fiona asked.

"I don't think so, but I daren't leave to find a phone box in case the bus comes."

Holiday Inn, Marriot, and Wyndham buses pulled up one after the other. A few lucky people boarded each one.

We sat down on our bags, now the only people remaining at the stop.

As each bus approached, we hopped up and read its light.

Car Park 1, Staff Car Park, Inter-terminal Transfer. Holiday Inn. Again.

"I wish we were staying at the Holiday Inn," I said, "I'm like a bloody kangaroo bouncing up and down all the time."

"Simon, it's here. Quick, don't let it go past." Fiona jumped up and waved at the bus. It stopped, and with a heartfelt hydraulic sigh, the doors swung open.

The plump lady driver gazed down at us from her perch.

"Y'all for the Comfort Inn?"

"Yep, just the two of us," I said.

Who are the rest of 'y'all'?

We heaved our bags up the steps and into the racks. The doors closed, and we plopped on to the seats.

45 seconds later the doors opened.

"Are we here?" I asked the driver.

"Yes, sir. Comfort Inn, right there. Y'all need help with your baggage?"

"We'll manage, thank you."

I strapped my backpack on, helped Fiona with her bag full of rocks and we stepped down.

"Far out, Simon, we could've walked here in three minutes instead of waiting for thirty."

"All right, all right, we weren't to know."

The bland homogenous same-everywhere-in-the-world hotel room felt cooler than the outside air. The air-conditioning unit above the bed vibrated as if there was a miniature motorcyclist trapped in the wall. I hoped it wouldn't drop off and kill us during the night.

"Now what are we going to do?" I said. "It's two in the morning, I don't feel the slightest bit like sleeping, we're supposed to visit Hollywood tomorrow, and I don't want to be tired for it."

"Are you hungry? My tummy thinks it's dinner time. I'll call room service."

I could hear Fiona's voice on the phone while I took a shower; her words muffled by the powerful hot jets.

"They must be used to international travellers wanting meals at strange times," she said, as I stood in the doorway towelling off, "there's a huge menu."

"I think you're going to find everywhere in America has a huge menu."

Twenty minutes later a knock at the door announced an elderly man in an ill-fitting uniform, carrying a tray. Plates peeked out from under a white linen cloth.

"Your meal, ma'am." He offered the tray to Fiona. She took it and made to close the door, but the man prevented it from shutting, and looked at her.

12.
Mopeds and Turtles

Fiona was terse with the night porter. "Yes, thank you. We don't need anything else."

I whispered, "He wants you to tip him."

"Tip him? Why?"

I fished in my wallet, and gave the man two dollars. He smiled thinly, nodded, and reversed out of the door.

Fiona looked puzzled. "What was that about?"

"In America you have to tip everyone. The salaries aren't very high, so employees top up their income with tips. Porters, waiting staff, taxi drivers, even hairdressers expect it. In fact, I don't think I gave him enough."

"Gosh, I didn't realise," she said. "We must make sure we've got a wodge of dollar bills with us. What a funny system. It's not like that in England, is it? Or New Zealand."

We removed the cloth from the tray. Underneath were two cowpat-sized burgers, a side of chips, a large dill pickle, and a can of root beer each.

"I asked for two burgers, with chips and a drink," said Fiona. "We could have had one between us."

The smell of the food made me feel hungry, and I picked at the chips.

"These are normal American portions," I said. "On my last visit here, I gained about ten pounds in a fortnight."

We spent two days in Los Angeles, and fought the jetlag long enough to experience Disneyland and Hollywood. We also spent significantly more time than I would have ever thought possible, indiscriminately fondling clothes in shopping malls. Fiona loved the shops in America, and complained we hadn't planned to stay longer.

"Don't forget we were on a tight budget, so I only booked two nights," I said. "I wish we'd known about my extra six months redundancy payment at that point."

"We'll have to come back. I've decided I love America."

We returned to the airport, and boarded the next flight to Hawaii.

"How come we didn't have to show our passports?" asked Fiona.

"This is a domestic flight, there's no immigration."

"Of course. I keep forgetting Hawaii isn't a separate country."

We hefted our carry-on luggage down the aisle of another Air New Zealand flight, with plenty of Kiwi accents on board. This time Fiona wasn't related to our seat neighbours as they came from Auckland, New Zealand's largest city. I gathered this was a different solar system in the opinion of rural South Island residents.

≈ ≈ ≈

I love this tropical holiday sensation. The warm wet air, the smell of damp earth, the shiny wet vegetation.

As we walked through Honolulu airport terminal, the sound of steel guitars in the distance added to the exotic feeling. A band in traditional dress played a welcome song. Grass-skirted ladies gyrated their hips in front of the musicians. Fiona grabbed my hand and began dancing round our luggage to the music. One of the smiling dancers brought flower *leis,* and hung them round our necks.

Fiona squeezed into the rear door of the hotel shuttle bus with several generously proportioned American tourists.

"Sorry, Simon," she said, "There's no room back here, you'll have to sit in the front with the driver."

I opened the buses front door and found myself face-to-face with a laughing brown islander, squashed behind the steering wheel.

"English, right? The passenger door's on the other side in America."

Oops.

I ran around the front of the bus, hoping no-one else had seen the stupid limey.

The driver's banana-sized fingers tapped on the steering wheel, and he hummed to himself as he drove. I started a conversation with him.

"Are you a native Hawaiian?"

"Well, I've lived here a long time, but I'm originally from Tonga."

My first real live Tongan. We're getting nearer.

"How come you moved from Tonga?"

"There's no work, really. Some of my family still live there, but they mostly grow their own vegetables and keep chickens, they don't work much. Some people have two or three part-time jobs, just to survive. I miss Tonga, but the money's great in Honolulu, and I can fly home at least once a year to see them."

"We're flying to Tonga the day after tomorrow."

"You are? Where are you staying? You can stay with my family if you like. They live in Nuku'alofa. Just say Isy in Hawaii sent you. I'm Isilele, but everyone calls me Isy."

"That's very kind of you, Isy. We've accommodation sorted out, thanks." I wasn't used to this extreme friendliness of Tongans yet.

I had a very important question I wanted to ask the first real live Tongan I'd met.

"Have you ever seen the Queen of Tonga?"

He laughed again. Isy was a cheerful man.

"I've seen her many times. When I last flew home she was at the airport, flying to New Zealand on the same plane I had arrived on. I think she spends most of her life in Auckland."

This was a blow. It'd be disappointing if we were in Tonga, and she wasn't.

"How could I find out whether she's in the country?" I asked.

Another huge laugh.

"Ask any of the airport workers. They might know whether she's due in or out."

≈ ≈ ≈

Isy dropped us at the open-air reception of the Sands Bay Hotel. Fiona selected a few brochures from a display riffling in the tropical breeze. They advertised everything from surfing waves taller than skyscrapers, to helicopter flights over dramatically exploding volcanoes. A direct correlation existed between the price of the excursion, and the likelihood of you not returning alive.

"I wish we were here longer," said Fiona, "look at all the attractions. We won't have time to fly to the other islands, will we?"

"Not this visit, unfortunately."

The receptionist handed me our key.

I quizzed her. "We fly out tomorrow night, so we haven't got much time here. Can you recommend some things to do that don't involve dying too much?"

"How about snorkelling?" she said. "Hanauma Bay has the clearest water, and if you're lucky, you'll see turtles and all the colourful fish. You can rent snorkels there. How does that sound for tomorrow morning?"

Fiona turned to me. "I'd love to try snorkelling. You're always enthusiastic about it."

The receptionist continued proposing our comprehensive and exciting itinerary.

"In the evening you could take a tour to a *Luau*."

"What's a Luau?" I asked.

"It's a traditional Hawaiian feast, an all-you-can-eat buffet with a Hawaiian show and dancing. They'll pick you up and drop you back here on a fully air-conditioned bus. It leaves at 5 p.m."

Fiona licked her lips. "That's dinner tomorrow night sorted."

"Okay," I said, "those don't sound too fatal. Can you book us on to that tour?"

"Sure," said the receptionist. "It's eighty dollars each, including the transfers. I'll put it on your room."

"Thanks. How do we get to the snorkelling?"

"You can either catch a bus from Waikiki Beach; it's about a 30-minute ride, or if you want a bit of fun, you could rent a couple of mopeds from us."

I turned to Fiona. "What d'you reckon? Shall we rent a moped? Then we'd be able to stop on the way if we pass something else to look at."

"I've never ridden one, Simon. I'm not sure in a big city, on the wrong side of the road, is the best place to learn. When I was a kid on the farm, I fell off the back of my brother's motorbike, and it put me off a bit."

The receptionist was keen for us to hire one. "They're really easy to ride, there's a cycle track you're allowed to ride on, they don't go fast, and they're such fun."

"All right," said Fiona, "I'll give it a go."

Our luggage had discovered where the lift was and which button to press, and had beaten us to our room. We found it had also managed to climb on a shelf ready for us to unpack.

"The cars are so tiny," said Fiona, as we stood on the balcony. "It's funny being above the tops of the palm trees."

Orange sky over the sea gave way to pitch blackness.

"It gets dark fast here, doesn't it?" I said, "I suppose we're nearer the equator."

"Where shall we go for dinner?"

"I noticed an American institution we passed, before we arrived at the hotel. Let me initiate you in the wonders of Denny's."

"Do I need to dress up?"

I laughed. "T-shirt and shorts is fine for Denny's."

≈ ≈ ≈

The tropical night breeze tingled our skin as we sat in the first-floor restaurant.

"I haven't been in a restaurant without walls before," said Fiona, gazing out at the floodlights illuminating the underside of the palm fronds.

She studied the list of food on offer, which had more entries than the Honolulu street directory.

"There's so much choice. I've no idea how I'm going to decide," she said.

The server approached and filled our glasses with iced water.

"Hi, I'm Renée, I'll be your waitress this evening. Do you need any help with the menu?"

Fiona ran her finger down the front page.

"What's the nicest local dish? I want to try something Hawaiian."

"If you enjoy fish," said Renée, "I can recommend the *Mahi-Mahi* with macadamia nuts. Hawaiian boats catch it just offshore, and they grow the nuts on The Big Island, near Hilo."

"That sounds exactly what I feel like."

Fiona ordered the Mahi-Mahi, and I settled for American baby back pork ribs.

We held hands across the table and gazed into the warm night. The noise of tourist buses participating in a competition to find the world's loudest horn accompanied the rustle of palm trees.

Fiona looked pensive. "We have to return here for a longer visit too."

"Just think," I said, "tomorrow night we're taking off for Tonga and more adventures."

"I'm looking forward to seeing a bit of Hawaii first," she said.

≈ ≈ ≈

Fiona lay in the morning sun on our balcony reading a book, her bare legs propped on a table. I sat up in bed and blinked, rubbing my eyes with clenched fists.

"Morning sleepyhead," she said. "D'you want any breakfast? I don't think I can eat anything after the enormous meal last night."

"Hiya! You're in holiday mode already."

"I love this heat. Rise and shine, we've got a date with a moped."

The receptionist directed us to the rear of the hotel. I had my snorkel gear with me; Fiona would need to rent some at the bay. We found the moped man, we signed a waiver, and he gave us an overview of the controls that was so brief it was finished before I realised he'd started.

"Can I have a helmet?" asked Fiona. "I'm not very confident about this."

This request surprised the rental man.

"You don't need one in Hawaii. State law doesn't require it."

"I want one anyway. What happens if I fall off?"

The moped man found a helmet for Fiona last used by Biggles, and we mounted our steeds.

The occasional car passed us, as we discovered the beach road cycle path. Palm trees fringed the sea, waves broke on rocks. Diamond Head's distant peak showed the route we'd take to Hanauma Bay.

Fiona trundled along. I slowed down to wait for her.

"We'd be a lot quicker if you sped up a bit."

"I've never done this, Simon. It's a bit scary."

An elderly lady on a bicycle overtook us easily.

"I think you'd find it less wobbly if you did over ten miles an hour," I said.

Fiona became braver, and by the time we reached Hanauma Bay she was flying along, frustrated by the moped's top speed.

"Very good, Evel Knievel," I said, "we're here now, time to get off."

"I don't want to get off. I might not get going again."

≈ ≈ ≈

We parked the mopeds, and jumped down the steps on to the beach.

"There are long lines for snorkel hire," I said. "We'll struggle to find a spare spot of sea, with all these people."

"Is it always this busy?" Fiona asked the vendor, once we'd reached the front of the queue.

"Bus tours. Wait until you see underwater, and you'll understand why everyone comes here."

He handed Fiona a mask, snorkel, and fins.

"Here's my tip," he said, "swim beyond where all the big groups are splashing around in the shallows. You'll find the best fish there."

I put on my snorkel and helped Fiona attach hers. We waded in.

Fiona stuck her face in the water while standing chest-deep, and immediately surfaced, wide-eyed. She pointed at a group of fish.

"Look at those, Simon. The colours, this is amazing."

I remembered my first view of the underwater world, and I knew what she was experiencing.

Fiona discovered she couldn't breathe through the snorkel and call out at the same time.

"Simon, Simon! *glub*. Look, look! *glurble*. Did you see that fish? *splutter splutter*. Oh wow, a Turtle!"

I laughed. "You'll notice a lot more if you keep your face under."

We moved out to where we had the bay to ourselves, marvelling at the sea life's bright colours which would have shamed ITV's test card.

"Simon, I'm getting a bit cold. I think I've had enough."

"All right, let's swim back."

Fiona carried her snorkel and fins in one hand as she waded out. Her skin was shiny wet, and her hair was dripping down her front. I had never seen her in this pose. She looked dazzling, reminding me of Ursula Andress in the *James Bond* film.

"I loved snorkelling," she said, "I want to go another day."

"There'll be plenty more snorkelling in Tonga. We'd better buy you your own snorkel set."

"More stuff to carry. And I need some more clothes. We're going out for dinner tonight, remember."

"But we've got bags full of clothes," I said.

"I haven't brought enough of those loose light dresses. And I need another bikini. And we should buy you a Hawaiian shirt while we're here, even though they're dreadful on you. Who knows when we'll be back?"

I sighed. Fiona loved shopping. This could be a long afternoon.

We returned Fiona's snorkel gear, and asked the vendor the way to a shopping mall.

"Are you staying in Waikiki?" he asked.

"Yes, at the Sands Bay Hotel."

"The best place is Ala Moana shopping centre. It's a short walk from your hotel. There's a beautiful beach there too, quieter than Waikiki."

≈ ≈ ≈

We changed out of our wet swimmers and returned to the mopeds. This time, Fiona couldn't wait to mount hers, and set off without me.

We raced back to the hotel round the coast road, Fiona's helmet confidently strapped to the back of the moped. The warm wind in our faces made us holiday-happy. I caught her at a traffic light, and we looked into the distance.

"Is that rain up ahead?" she asked.

"Yep, prepare for a drenching."

Within minutes, the road had become a stream of dirty water, as the brief tropical rainstorm soaked us, transparent to our underwear. We slowed down, so we could see where we were going.

The rain stopped after a short while, and the ground steamed. I lifted my head and again breathed in the wonderful smell of tropical wet earth as we dried out quickly in the sun.

≈ ≈ ≈

We returned the mopeds, grabbed some chips, and took the lift to our room to eat them. Fiona changed out of her damp shorts into a bikini and a long flowing dress.

"I do need more of these, they're so practical," she said.

The receptionist drew the short walk to the Ala Moana shopping centre on a paper map. We escaped the bustle of tourist-busy Waikiki, and found the clothing emporium the other side of a bridge. Burt Bacharach played piano through ceiling speakers as, tasting the air-conditioning, we descended an escalator to a floor with an acre of Hawaiian shirts.

Fiona held shirt after shirt up against me. After twenty minutes of being a professional male model, I suggested we buy one. My shopping tolerance time wasn't as long as hers. Fiona disappeared into the changing rooms with an armful of dresses, appearing several times to ask my opinion.

I knew it wouldn't matter which ones I liked and which ones I didn't, she was going to buy the one she wanted to anyway. I just said I liked them all. Fiona complained this wasn't a very helpful approach.

We walked back via Ala Moana Park and beach, carrying our dresses, shirts, and Fiona's new snorkel kit. At three o'clock on a warm, humid afternoon I expected the beach to be packed as a commuter train on a Tuesday evening, but we had the sand all to ourselves.

"Come on, let's go swimming." Fiona threw off her dress and ran into the sea in her bikini.

I dropped the bags and joined her. We splashed in the water for a few minutes, and lay on the beach to dry off. Sand stuck to Fiona's tummy as she turned over, looking like an advert for Neutrogena sunscreen.

"This is perfect," she said, "do we have to leave? Can't we change our flight? I don't want to get on another plane yet."

13.
Crazy Tour Guide

"We can't change our flights, Fiona. We leave tonight. But don't worry, Tonga will be even more perfect."

"I hope so, Simon."

We returned to the hotel to dress for the evening's entertainment.

≈ ≈ ≈

The bus to the Luau was already full of passengers, and a brightly-coloured shirt with a Hawaiian man inside it escorted us up the steps. As the bus pulled out, he stood at the front speaking into a microphone.

A huge perma-grin decorated his face.

"Welcome, welcome, welcome everybody. My name is Randy, and I'll be your guide this evening. I'm 50 percent Hawaiian, 50 percent Cherokee Indian, 100 percent crazy tour guide."

This was going to be a full-on American experience.

"All right, I need to find out something about every one of you, we'll be best of friends before the night is done. Whereabouts are all you folks from?"

He started at the front.

"Sir, Madam? From New York? You'll be pleased how friendly everyone is in Hawaii. You, sir? Los Angeles? See the traffic outside the bus? It's the same as Los Angeles traffic, except here nobody's shooting at you."

He addressed every passenger as the bus sped along the highway, making mild fun of each of their home towns. So far, everyone was American.

We were next.

"Sir, where are you from?"

"London," I said.

"Oh. How is the queen?"

I nodded and replied that to the best of my knowledge Her Majesty wasn't currently suffering any serious ailments.

"I'm from New Zealand," shouted Fiona, feeling left out.

"New Zealand? You'll see some of your country's dancing tonight."

He moved on.

"Madam? Chicago? At least your hair will stay in place for over five minutes here. Sir? Seattle? It rains a bit in Hawaii every day, just to make you guys feel at home."

"What did he mean by my country's dancing?" Fiona asked me.

"No idea. The receptionist said there'd be dancing. I thought she meant Hawaiian dancing."

Randy finished his comedy act, and as the sun set, we arrived at the Luau.

We observed an entire roast pig being pulled out of an underground oven by two shirtless Hawaiians. The pig departed for an appointment it had arranged with a carving knife, and we lined up to collect our food and drink from a buffet.

A band of island men arrived on stage, dressed in bright Hawaiian shirts. Some were carrying guitars, and one sat at a drum kit. In front of the stage, a fire burned in a small trench. I jiggled in my seat as the upbeat music began. This annoyed Fiona.

"Sit still!" she said.

"I can't help it. The music makes me want to dance."

An invisible announcer spoke over the loudspeakers.

"Good evening, everyone. Welcome to the Luau. We'll start with traditional dancing from the Pacific islands. First, Hawaii."

The Hawaiian dancers took to the stage and began their routine, wiggling hips and twirling hands, as if they were on traffic duty at a fingernail varnish convention. The ladies had orange skirts, and tops made from two coconut halves.

"I like the bikini tops," I said to Fiona. "Let's buy you one of those."

"Very funny. The oiled-up men are pretty attractive though."

"Touché."

The announcer continued. "Next, dancers from Tahiti."

These costumes were less revealing, long dresses with bright yellow around their shoulders, and green skirts covering their legs. Enormous headdresses balanced on top, and I spent some time pondering how they managed to defy gravity.

Fiona appreciated their fashion. "One of those yellow and green dresses would suit me. I wonder if you can buy them in the gift shop?"

"We bought enough dresses at Ala Moana to keep you going until your grandchildren's weddings."

"Now," said the announcer, "dancers from New Zealand."

Five bare-chested muscly men took to the stage and performed a war dance routine. They had tattoos on their upper bodies and faces, and large green stones hung round their necks. Eyes wide, they challenged the crowd with threatening movements, and stuck their tongues out so far, I thought they were going to fall off.

"It's like the start of the rugby," said Fiona, clapping and shouting, "Kiwi, Kiwi!".

I realised the traditional English view of New Zealand being an offshoot of Australia was inaccurate. New Zealand culture was more closely linked to these Pacific islands.

"Lastly, the Samoan fire dance."

The music stopped. There was a brief dramatic silence, followed by a single repeated drum.

A near-naked warrior approached the fire pit carrying a stick, while other Samoan men assembled behind him. Each brandished a flaming torch. Hundreds of Americans augmented the drum sound by clicking their cameras, as if they were paparazzi sighting George Clooney with a new girlfriend.

The warrior ran through the fire, and as the music restarted, he thrust his stick into the flames, lighting both ends. He spun the stick round again and again as the drumming became more and more urgent, throwing the flaming pole into the air and catching it. The crowd clapped and cheered.

Once the show had finished, a staff member invited us to meet the dancers.

Fiona led me over to the New Zealand group, and they posed with us while an employee took a photo with our camera.

"Where are you from?" Fiona asked the bare-chested Maori next to her.

"I'm from the North Island of New Zealand, a place called Whangarei."

"I'm from the West Coast of the South Island," she said.

"Choice, Bro!" he said, using a phrase commonly spoken by Maori. "Some of my family live there, the Taumatas. D'you know them?"

"I went to school with one of them, the older boy."

I rolled my eyes. The South Island of New Zealand really was a village.

≈ ≈ ≈

1 a.m. found us sitting in the open-air reception in T-shirts and shorts, waiting for the shuttle bus back to the airport. As Ben had explained to me, flights between Pacific islands always take off at a time when most people are customarily fast asleep. Flight NZ59 was no exception, with a 4 a.m. departure time. It was a warm, clear night, and we sat on our bags, quiet with anticipation.

I was overjoyed to discover the shuttle-bus driver was once more my Tongan friend Isy. He greeted us with a laugh.

"Hello you two, leaving so soon?"

"We'll be in Tonga later on today." I could scarcely believe what I was saying.

I made sure I sat next to Isy again.

"Isy, tell me the most important thing to do and see in Nuku'alofa. A real cultural experience."

"Well, they do traditional dancing at the Tongan National Centre, with Tongan food and everything. The tourists seem to like that." He laughed again, his vast belly engulfing the steering wheel to the point I became concerned about his ability to rotate it.

"Hmm, okay. I went to something similar at the Luau here a few hours ago. But what about a real Tongan experience most tourists would never see?"

"If you're asked to attend a Tongan feast, don't turn down the invitation. There's nothing like it. And we love having westerners at our feasts, they'll make a real fuss of you."

"I hope we get that opportunity. Anything else?"

"For something unique, go to the cinema."

"The cinema?" I asked, "do they show Tongan films?"

Isy found this funny.

"Oh no, there's no Tongan films. It'll be an American movie, but it's not the film that's the attraction."

I promised to visit the movies, although I wasn't sure what he meant. We arrived at the airport and he pulled our bags out.

"Bye Isy." I shook his huge hand.

"You guys have the best time in my homeland. I'll be thinking of you."

He squeezed back into the front seat and drove off, laughing to himself.

"They seem such friendly people, don't they?" said Fiona.

≈ ≈ ≈

The middle of the night at Honolulu airport.

Warm.

Tropical.

Chaotic.

If these passengers had been English or Americans, they'd have been tired and grumpy. The English might have been moaning at their spouses, the Americans shouting, 'Hell, what's all this carry-on? I just wanna board my plane.'

These people were Tongans, grinning, hugging each other, kissing each other's children. Check-in was just another social gathering with the extended family.

It's no wonder people call Tonga The Friendly Isles.

The queue stretched to the entrance doors, and we joined the rear of a large musical group, travelling with their instruments, all wearing the blue-and-white band uniform.

Fiona left me with the bags while she inspected the airport shops, in the event she needed any more emergency dresses.

A slim young musician waiting in line turned to me. "Hello, are you going to Tonga?"

"I am, I'm staying for six weeks with my girlfriend, she's just off looking at the shops. I take it you're a band of some sort?"

"Yes, we've been playing in the finals of the Pacific Islands Silver Band Competition here in Honolulu."

"Wow, did you win?" I asked.

"No, Tahiti won, but we came second. It's the first time a Tongan band made the finals."

"Congratulations. And now you're all going home."

"We are, it's been so exciting. Most of us have never left Tonga. Anyway, I'm Tomasi. Nice to meet you."

I introduced myself, and quizzed him a bit more about his home country.

"Tomasi, what should we see in Tonga, for a real bit of local culture?"

"Well, the Tongan National Centre has traditional dancing in the evenings…"

I stopped him, more rudely than I intended. "I know, I've been told about that. But I don't mean a tourist experience. I mean a real Tongan experience. Something only Tongans go to."

"Church. You must go to church. Everyone in Tonga goes to church; people have a low opinion of you if you miss it. In fact, on Sunday in Tonga, church is the only activity. We can't play rugby on Sunday, or go shopping, or even drive a car."

"Wow, I didn't realise Tongan society was so strict."

"It's only Sundays. Even the shops can't open on the Lord's day. My band plays at church. You must come to church with me."

"We'd love to," I said. "Which one do you perform at?"

"We play at the main Wesleyan church in Pangai every Sunday. Are you going to Pangai?"

"That's the town in the Ha'apai Islands, right? We'll be staying there for ten days after a few weeks in Nuku'alofa."

"You might be there at the same time as the king. He's visiting Pangai for the first time in years. There'll be celebrations and feasts, and I'm so proud my band will be playing at church for him."

"Tomasi, d'you know if the queen will be with him?"

"I'm not sure, they both stay in New Zealand, we don't see them often. Anyway, if you find me after the service, I'll introduce you to my family."

Tomasi's band was at the front of the queue, and were checking in their various instruments. In place of suitcases, many of the Tongans had multiple cardboard boxes tied up with string. They'd stripped the shelves of the Hawaiian electronics stores, and they loaded televisions, food mixers and power tools all in their original boxes on to the baggage weighing scales. On the next desk to ours, a man was told he didn't have the weight allowance for his ghetto blaster, so he removed it from the packaging, and carried it as cabin baggage.

Tomasi turned back to me after checking in his trumpet, and I introduced him to Fiona, who'd returned from feeling every item in the airport's stores.

"Looks like everyone's been shopping," he said, "see you in Tonga."

≈ ≈ ≈

Our heavy backpacks weren't out of place among the mounds of luggage, no-one was travelling light. We passed through border control without incident, and entered the departure lounge. Fiona discovered a further anthology of shops here, and vanished again, while I sat at the gate surrounded by Tongans. I dipped into our travel guide at the section concerning religion.

Christianity, it said, was the default. If you were anything but a Christian, it was best to keep this quiet. There were multiple denominations to choose from: Catholics, Methodists, Seventh Day Adventists. The Wesleyans appeared to be winning the 'bottoms on pews' race, the king being their most prominent exponent (and their most important bottom). Schools funded by the churches educated almost all the children. The churches were able to impose the threat on families, no church donation; no children's education.

After a few minutes two pairs of hot-pants joined me, each containing a young blonde European girl carrying a small backpack. This distracted me from the guide, and I greeted them, as fellow travellers do when they're miles from home.

"Hello, I'm Simon. Are you both going to Tonga?"

I sound like an idiot. Of course they're going to Tonga. They're at the gate for the Tongan flight.

"Hallo," said the taller one. "I'm Anja, she's Claudia. We're visiting Tonga and then going to New Zealand for a year. What about you?" She spoke English with an accent, she pronounced 'what' as *vot.*

"I'm staying in Tonga for six weeks, then also going to New Zealand. Where are you from?"

"We're from Hamburg, we've been travelling round America for three months."

"Where are you staying in Tonga?"

Anja spoke again.

Claudia doesn't say anything. What's wrong with her?

"We don't know. We'll find somewhere when we get there."

"I know a place called Toni's backpackers," I informed them, as if I was a seasoned Tongan travel expert. "I'm sure he'll have room for you. He'll be waiting at the airport and can give us all a ride." I hoped Toni would be able to deliver the services his on-the-spot Honolulu airport agent had just sold.

"*Danke* (Thanks)," said Anja, "that sounds good."

Fiona returned from the shops. I had that sudden guilty feeling men get when their partners catch them talking to an attractive girl.

She glared at me, unimpressed with my choice of acquaintance.

14.
A Non-existent Day

"This is Fiona, she's my girlfriend," I said, in case anyone was in doubt we were a couple. Including Fiona herself.

Anja introduced herself and Claudia, who still hadn't said a word.

"Kia ora, Ladies and Gentlemen. Thank you for your patience. Welcome to flight NZ59 to Nuku'alofa. We would like to begin by boarding families with young children. First and business class passengers may board at any time. If you are seated in economy class, please relax for now."

"Fiona, what does 'Kia ora' mean?" I asked.

"It's a Maori greeting. They say it before every New Zealand flight."

"Oh. I hadn't noticed before. The announcer has a strong New Zealand accent, doesn't she?"

We waited obediently. The Tongans reshuffled their assorted babies and ghetto blasters, and prepared to queue up.

General boarding opened with the usual race to be first. We stood behind the German girls. As we walked down the air bridge, I noticed Tomasi further ahead, and he waved at me and grinned.

I hope Anja and Claudia saw that.

A family party was in full flow on the plane. Nobody was interested in taking their seats. Everyone walked up and down the aisles, greeted old friends, hugged people, and laughed continually. Huge-tummied men and women squeezed past each other, their bellies merging in mutual compression. Eventually the steward persuaded everyone to sit in their own seat, and flight NZ59 to Nuku'alofa was airborne.

Nuku'alofa.

The abode of love.

The abode of the Queen of Tonga.

≈ ≈ ≈

The snorkelling at Hanauma Bay seemed an age ago, yet we hadn't slept since. We were both in uncomfortable positions. Fiona had scrunched herself into a ball with her head on my lap, and my head nodded unsupported in mid-air like a toy bulldog on a car dashboard, in and out of consciousness.

The smell of incinerated airline food behind us woke me up shortly before the cabin crew turned on the lights, and it made me feel hungry. Fiona snuggled into my arm.

"Do you realise," I said, "we lost an entire day crossing the dateline. Yesterday never existed for us."

"I wish I'd been asleep all that time. An extra 24 hours would be great now."

Fiona didn't want her breakfast of scrambled eggs, bacon and sausage, so I ate both of them. As soon as he'd cleared the trays away, the steward announced we should return to our seats, we'd soon land in Nuku'alofa.

I strained forward to view the islands I had been preparing to visit all my life, but below us I only saw a blanket of cotton-wool cloud with occasional small sea-coloured holes in it. The plane descended, and the white mist swaddled us. I had no idea how the pilots could see where they were going.

"Cabin crew, prepare cabin for landing. Ladies and Gentlemen, the seatbelt sign has been switched on. Please ensure your seat back is upright, your tray table is stowed away, and your armrest is down."

The plane fell out of the bottom of the cloud, and endless water extended in all directions to an infinite horizon. Our ear sensation told us we were descending. The wheels *whirr-whirred* as they disengaged beneath us.

Water, water, everywhere, and not a drop to drink.

"Cabin crew, take your seats for landing."

This meant there was a few minutes until we touched down.

Where's the ground?

As I became convinced the plane was landing in the sea, and we were going to die spectacularly in a newsworthy blaze of exploding aviation fuel, palm trees appeared, and a cleared area with a fence round it. The plane landed, and as if a pause button had been released, the passengers cheered and started talking to each other.

We were all on Tongan soil, some of us for the first time.

≈ ≈ ≈

As soon as the cabin crew extinguished the seatbelt sign, everyone stood up and started gathering their belongings.

A Tongan man pointed out of the window and addressed me. "My family. They've come to meet me."

A group of about twenty adults, children, babies, and old ladies, stood behind a low fence near the edge of the runway, staring at our plane.

"Are they all your family?" I asked.

The nuance of my meaning escaped him.

"Oh, no, a few had to stay behind as there wasn't enough room in the truck."

Truck.

I looked at the tarmac between the plane and the terminal.

That's what's different about this airport. No trucks.

Several workers dressed in white overalls pushed a set of steps up to the plane door.

Another three men wheeled two huge baggage carts towards the rear of the plane.

How will they cope with unloading all the instruments, televisions and other cardboard boxes by hand?

Manual labour performed every task at this airport. I remembered what Ben had said about third world travel being different.

The doors opened and the passengers at the front of the plane began to move. I woke Fiona, and we organised ourselves. The German girls stood several rows behind us, their blonde heads bending under the overhead lockers.

I paused at the top of the aeroplane steps. I had never disembarked from a plane without an air bridge, and I wanted to wave and shout "Good morning, Tonga!" as if I was Bill Clinton arriving for a presidential visit. At the bottom I turned to Fiona, who was looking sleepy.

"We're here, we're finally here," I said, "can you believe it?"

"Mmmm," she said, "I hope it's everything you're expecting."

≈ ≈ ≈

Pandemonium.

Chaos.

No baggage carousel.

No modern infrastructure.

As each baggage trolley arrived, the men in white unloaded it by tipping it on to the floor. They distributed cardboard boxes, televisions, power tools, and microwaves liberally over the arrivals hall. Tongans clambered over the pile, picking up bags, shouting at their friends.

How do they distinguish their own stringed-up cardboard boxes from everyone else's?

"Here's one of ours." Fiona shouted behind me, identifying a holdall I had missed.

Once the televisions and boxes were matched up with their owners, we found our other three bags together. I was glad we had backpacks; there were no trolleys apart from one rather sad two-wheeled one which had been ignored for decades. We shouldered our packs and joined the queue to leave the terminal.

A huge Tongan greeted us at immigration and customs, and took our passports more gently than his size suggested was possible. He didn't seem sure what to do with them. He looked up at us and grinned.

Tongans do a lot of grinning.

"How long will you be in Tonga?"

"Six weeks," I said.

"Great, you'll be able to see so much. Are you staying somewhere nice?"

He was so personable, I had to remember I was dealing with a government official.

"We're staying at Toni's backpackers to start."

"Very good."

He looked left, then right, he didn't want anyone else to hear what he was about to say. "Are you bringing in any guns, drugs or pornography?"

The relief showed on his face. He'd successfully delivered that question on his interrogation list. I admitted we didn't, in fact, have any guns, drugs or pornography, and wondered how he'd have coped if I'd answered "yes" to any of those. I thought of something I should ask him.

"Do you know if the queen is in Tonga?"

"No, she flew out to New Zealand some time ago. I think she'll be back in a couple of weeks." He paused and whispered guiltily, "I probably wasn't supposed to tell you that."

I intimated his secret of national security was safe with us. He stamped our passports and waved us through.

I looked over my shoulder for Anja and Claudia.

"Who are you looking for?" asked Fiona.

"Oh, just those German girls. I was going to help them find Toni."

"I'm sure they're capable of sorting out their own travel arrangements, Simon."

≈ ≈ ≈

Economic exile was the primary contributor to human traffic between the US and Tonga. Each week, the Air New Zealand plane from Honolulu heralded the importation of more televisions, more microwaves, and more money for everyone.

The throng of Tongans waited for their relatives. Anticipation gave way to celebration, as each expectant family embraced their prodigal sons.

We slipped through the crowd and exited the terminal. The sun burned my unprotected skin, as I lifted a hand to shield my eyes and search for Toni's sign.

I still had this firm image in my mind of a rural Yorkshireman. But nobody resembled a northern English farmer. Everyone was Tongan.

Someone touched my shoulder, and I swung round to find Tomasi, clutching his trumpet case.

"Hello, you two, did you have a pleasant flight?"

"Yes thank you, Tomasi. Are you flying to the Ha'apai Islands straight away, or staying in Nuku'alofa for a bit?"

"We're not flying to Ha'apai," he said, "we're going on the *Fokololo 'oe Hau.*"

How am I ever going to pronounce these Tongan names?

Tomasi explained. "It's a boat that travels between the islands. It's not as comfortable as flying, in fact we call it the 'floating coffin.' It's cheap, only twenty-five pa'anga. Where are you both staying?"

"Hopefully Toni's backpackers, but I can't see Toni anywhere."

Tomasi laughed. "I'll find him." He put his hands round his mouth, and turning in the direction of the car park outside the terminal shouted "Kesi, Kesi!"

What did Kesi mean? Was that Tongan for Toni?

"They're coming," said Tomasi.

A sturdy young Tongan lady pushed through the crowd towards us, clutching a handwritten sign. She wore a full-length patterned skirt, and her long dark pony tail cascaded down her black T-shirt, which advertised the 'San Francisco Forty-Niners'.

"Tomasi," she said, "have you been off on your travels? I hope you were a good boy. I heard you came second in your competition."

They hugged.

Everyone in Tonga seems to know each other.

"Kesi, I've brought some guests for you. You owe me commission."

Kesi laughed. "Get off with you, Tomasi. Go and play your trumpet."

Tomasi farewelled us. "Have an amazing holiday, please remember to come and find me in Ha'apai."

Kesi introduced herself.

"Hello, I'm Kesi. I work for Toni. Are you staying with us?"

Her sign said, 'Toni's Guest House'.

"Yes, I'm Simon, and this is my girlfriend Fiona. I phoned Toni, and he said he'd have room for us."

"Ah yes, we knew you were coming. Is there anyone else with you?"

"Hello, do you haff anywhere for us to stay?" said a familiar voice. I turned round to see we'd been followed.

"Kesi, this is Anja and Claudia, do you have enough beds for all of us?"

"No problem, no problem, bring your bags, room for everyone."

Kesi led the way through the throng of happy Tongan family and financial reunions.

Fiona looked at me strangely.

Have I done something wrong?

15.
Toni and Toni

"You didn't seem to have a problem remembering those German girls' names," said Fiona, giving me a steely glare.

An elderly beige minibus stood in the car park, reflecting the sun in its windows. The inscription *Toni's Guest House* ran down its side in large handwritten yellow letters. Kesi helped us and our luggage into the bus, and hoomphed herself up into the driver's seat.

Kesi turned the ignition key, and the starter motor issued a noise like a camel with severe laryngitis. The camel cleared its throat completely on the third attempt, and we reached a stately pace of twenty miles per hour, black smoke pouring from the exhaust. Our exit from the airport perimeter didn't result in us going any faster, and I concluded the bus had reached its top speed.

Trees with bright red flowers and luxuriant foliage competed for attention with large signs advertising unfamiliar companies. Cars in various stages of disrepair passed in the other direction, and Kesi waved and hooted at all of them. A pickup truck lacking both its doors and bonnet overtook us, crammed with waving smiling young Tongans riding in the tray.

I wanted to do that. It looked fun, and health and safety legislation didn't seem to have reached Tonga.

After about 30 minutes of trundling along the road, the scenery changed. Wooden houses with home-made extensions nailed on every side lined the route, covered in lurid coloured paint which helped them to stay upright. I assumed we'd entered a small village, but Kesi surprised me by announcing we'd arrived in Nuku'alofa.

Nuku'alofa.

The abode of love.

Love had never looked so run-down.

≈ ≈ ≈

Toni stood outside his guest house. He didn't resemble a Yorkshire farmer. He wore his long grey hair pulled back in a ponytail. I put his age around 50, and he was dressed in a pair of denim shorts of similar vintage. The smell of cigarette smoke accompanied his Caribbean hippy aura.

"Hey, guys, I'm Toni." He appeared to have just woken up.

"I'm Simon, this is Fiona, my girlfriend."

"Yes, yes, we knew you were coming, didn't know about Fiona, no matter, we'll move you to a double room."

Toni was fond of green. The outside of the guest house was spinach green, apart from the window and door frames, which were a darker shade.

Anja introduced herself and the still-silent Claudia, and we trooped inside with our bags.

The green theme continued throughout the communal kitchen and outdoor seating area, where there were several bright green wooden tables surrounded by green benches fixed around the perimeter.

Toni had painted our room in a colour that Dulux marketing might have named 'menthol cigarette packet'. A double bed with a mosquito net surrounding it stood in the centre, with a cupboard of an indeterminate era in the corner. The tiled floor echoed as we dumped our bags.

"How long d'you want to stay?" asked Toni.

"About four weeks, then we go to the Ha'apai Islands for ten days, then back here again. Is it okay to leave some of our bags here while we're in Ha'apai?"

"I should think so. Don't forget to come back for them, will you? You might not want to leave Ha'apai."

I assured him we wouldn't abandon our bags.

"What I really want right now," Fiona stated, "is a nice hot shower."

Toni found this extremely amusing. He laughed so hard he started to cough, a productive deep smoker's cough; the colour of his face changed to beetroot, and I worried he was going to collapse in front of us.

He recovered, and offered us a wide nicotine-coloured smile like the keys of a honky-tonk piano.

"You'll be waiting a long time for that, young lady."

"Why?" asked Fiona, unsure why her request was funny, "is there a queue for the shower or something?"

"There are no hot showers here. No hot showers anywhere in Tonga. Just cold. Except maybe at the International Pacific Hotel. But with the humid weather you don't need them. I'll show you where the bathrooms are."

The basic facilities comprised three shower heads and a sink, in an area with a blue tiled floor. Toni's green paintbrush hadn't discovered this room yet. Fiona and I grabbed our towels and washbags, and jumped in two showers next to each other.

"Brrrr" emanated from Fiona's cubicle. "Brrrrrrrr." Her shower lasted for 30 seconds.

The noises changed to rapid towel rubbing. "I'm not sure I'm going to survive this for six weeks. How do the Tongans manage?"

"You'll warm up once you stand in the sun for a bit."

Fiona sprinted to our room. I took a bit longer. I didn't care about the cold showers. My education had been at an English boarding school, so I was quite used to them.

≈ ≈ ≈

Fiona wasn't in the bedroom when I returned. I found her in the outdoor seating area, with a baby on her lap.

"Hello Simon, meet Toni." She poked the baby at me. "Isn't he cute?"

"Toni?" I asked.

I had this weird thought we'd gone back 50 years through a time machine, and our landlord had regressed to infancy.

"He's Kesi's baby," said Fiona. "She must have named him after the other Toni."

"Oh. Very nice. Where's Kesi?"

"She went to the shop. She'll be back in ten minutes."

People trust Fiona. Even with their babies. I don't know anything about babies.

"What are we supposed to do with…. Toni, while she's out?" I asked.

"Hold him and talk to him. Here, you have a go."

She passed Toni to me. He grizzled in my inexperienced arms. I gave him back.

"He prefers you," I said. "Babies don't seem to like me."

"I've never seen you with a baby before."

"Who's baby Toni's father?" I asked. "He looks fully Tongan, so I'm sure it's not Toni senior."

"Must be Kesi's husband, they both live here on site. She said he works at the palace."

"Maybe he'll know when the queen is in the country."

Kesi returned and relieved us of Toni junior.

"What does your husband do at the palace?" I asked her.

"He's the king's personal masseur, but the king isn't here now, so he's not working. He does a few odd jobs to keep busy, while the king's abroad."

"Would he know when their majesties are in the country?"

"Not really. The king's secretary calls him when he's needed, and he has to go straight away."

Kesi carted baby Toni off for a sleep.

"What d'you want to do first?" asked Fiona. "It's almost lunchtime."

"Let's explore the local area before jetlag kicks in."

≈ ≈ ≈

Rusty ships that hadn't moved in years were anchored offshore, cranes that had last functioned decades previously stood guard over silted-up wharves. Shallow mud flats stretched away from a narrow beach, decorated beautifully with lumps of old concrete and disused tins. Tongan men sat in small groups. They weren't talking, or reading, or doing anything productive. They were just sitting on the ground. The further we walked along the waterfront, the more decrepit the scene became.

The small number of westerners we encountered in the town centre waved and smiled as we passed. This felt a bit wrong. We were only acknowledging each other because of our common skin colour.

Some young Tongans called out "*Malo 'e leilei,"* (hello) to us, and turned to their friends, laughing. We returned the traditional greeting, to many smiles on both sides.

They continued, "Where are you from, where are you from?"

A man exited the sea, fully clothed, carrying a crab pot. "*Malo 'e leilei,*" he said.

We replied, demonstrating our newly learnt language skills.

"What have you caught?" Fiona asked.

"I've got my dinner." He smiled, and showed us the two large crabs in his pot. Every Tongan we'd met had impressed us with their ability to converse in basic English.

Further along the sea front, we passed a hand-painted wooden sign speared into the ground. It advertised *Octopus Dive School,* and pointed along a track leading away from the sea.

"D'you mind if we have a quick look here?" I asked.

At the end of a short path, we found a small yellow wooden house. A thin white man with a moustache knelt on the veranda, a spanner in his hand, studying part of an engine that was in pieces. He looked up.

"Hello, is this Octopus Dive School?" I asked him.

The man stood. He was tall, with dishevelled brown hair. "It is. Did you want to go diving?"

He'd a slight accent which I couldn't place.

"Yes, we're here for a few weeks and I was hoping I could do a few dives. I have my certification."

"We can do that."

He introduced himself as Jan, pronouncing it 'Yaan'.

"You're not a mechanic, are you?" he asked, "I can offer you some free diving if you can fix this alternator."

"Sorry, I don't know much about engines."

"No matter, I'll mend it eventually. When would you like to go? The weather will be perfect tomorrow."

I turned to Fiona, "Are you okay with me going diving tomorrow?"

"You enjoy yourself. I want to relax in the heat."

"Sounds like that works, Jan," I said.

"All right, I'll pick you up at nine. Where are you staying?"

"We're at Toni's Guest House."

"See you tomorrow."

Jan returned to his alternator.

≈ ≈ ≈

Cars lined both sides of the main street in the centre of Nuku'alofa. We discovered a shop on a corner named Elsie Sweet Store and Taxi.

"I'm hungry," said Fiona.

"Me too. I wonder what Elsie has for lunch."

Displayed on two white plastic tables outside Elsie's, a small selection of home-grown food interested us. A man wearing a singlet sat behind the first table. Fiona picked up a chunk of a white root vegetable and held it up.

"What's this called?" she asked him.

"*Taro*. Very good."

Neither of us appeared to have a copy of *Delia Smith's Easy Taro Recipes* with us, so we moved to the next table. The vendor sitting behind it wore a brown and yellow open-necked shirt. His table contained pineapples and bananas. As these were more recognisable, we bought two of each.

Elsie sold hot food and ice creams. We settled for a burger and chips. It didn't seem to be authentic Tongan cuisine, but apart from taro, I wasn't sure what was. The juicy freshly cooked burgers were a significant improvement on the mass-produced offerings available in western take-aways. After eating some bananas for dessert, we continued back to Toni's. Jetlag was kicking in, and, coupled with the giant burgers, we needed a siesta.

We were asleep, on top of the sheet, naked and sweltering, in minutes.

≈ ≈ ≈

I was drowning in a salty swimming pool, a saturated cloth engulfing my face, stealing my last breath as I reached for the surface with one hand. "Help, help!" No sound came from my mouth. How could I make anyone hear?

I opened my eyes, and remembered where I was.

"Yuck," announced Fiona next to me, shiny sweat pouring off her back. "I'm going for another shower. I can understand now why they're cold."

"All right. I'll have one later. I'm only going to get sweaty again."

I towelled off, pulled on a T-shirt and shorts, and headed to the kitchen to find bottled water. As I poured some into a glass, I realised I wasn't alone. In the corner of the outdoor seating area sat Claudia, with baby Toni on her lap. There was no sign of Anja.

"Hello," I said to her, "I see you're looking after Toni."

"Hallo, I am Claudia." Her strong German accent spoke the first words I had ever heard her say. She had a friendly smile, and her eyes shone above sunburnt freckles.

"I'm Simon. Where's Anja today?"

Claudia's expression changed. She shrugged slightly. "I don't know."

"I thought you two went everywhere together."

The silent Claudia had an outburst. It had been building up for some time.

"I don't haff good English. She talk for me. She make me not happy. Ve always do vot she vont."

She paused, frowning, and stared at Toni junior. He mirrored her expression.

"Ven ve get to New Zealant, I don't vont to see her again."

She hugged baby Toni like a hot water bottle, as if he were going to offer some comfort.

At that moment Anja entered and gave me a dismissive evil eye. She clearly monitored who Claudia was permitted to fraternise with, and I wasn't on the approved list. She addressed Claudia in a stream of rapid aggressive German I failed to understand.

Claudia obediently stood up. Her attractive smile was long gone.

I realised with mild panic if Anja dragged Claudia away, I'd be the one left holding the baby. Quite literally.

Claudia passed Toni junior to me. He stuck out his bottom lip and gripped my T-shirt. His strength surprised me, and I prayed silently I could keep him from howling until someone came to my rescue.

Claudia followed Anja without looking back. I felt sorry for her, but now I had an extremely serious situation of my own.

I was sitting by myself, 10,000 miles from home, with an unfamiliar baby on my lap.

16.
Plooop

Toni junior started to sob.

No, no, please, not now.

I jiggled him up and down.

I pulled funny faces.

I made strange noises.

Nope, I could tell he was building up to a wail. And three–two–one–

"WAAAAAAAAAAAAH."

The noise brought Kesi in, followed by Fiona. I'd never been more relieved to see either of them. Kesi took Toni from me, and stuffed a bottle in his mouth.

As Toni junior sucked noisily, Kesi asked, "Will you be having dinner here? I can make you a burger and chips."

"We had a burger for lunch, thanks," I said.

Is burger and chips the staple Tongan meal?

"I think we'll go out," said Fiona.

"There's a nice Chinese restaurant in town called Fakalato," said Kesi. "My cousin, Eileen, owns it."

"D'you fancy Chinese?" I asked Fiona.

"Why not? Seems as Tongan as anything."

≈ ≈ ≈

Nuku'alofa's street lighting sporadically lit the way as we headed to the restaurant. We carefully negotiated the broken pavements, avoiding multiple dogs of assorted lineage, running, barking, fighting, mating. A lot of them were obviously male.

"Are we here?" I asked.

Steep stairs led to the premises above a shop.

On the first floor we entered a dimly lit room. Red paper Chinese lanterns hung from the ceiling, and disposable table coverings hid cheap plastic furniture.

We were the only clientele. The menu advertised each dish in small, medium, and large sizes. This was a novel dining concept I had never considered before. We ordered a small soup each to start, and two small meat dishes and a small rice for the main.

While we waited for the soup, I explained Claudia's situation to Fiona.

"Poor girl," said Fiona, "Anja's a bully. I disliked her from first sight. I always felt she was looking down on me."

"Well, she is about six feet tall."

"You know what I mean," said Fiona, failing to appreciate my humour.

The waitress placed two gigantic bowls in front of us.

"Thanks," I said, "but we ordered two small soups."

"Yes sir, those are small soups."

I gazed at the washing-up bowls on the table, and wondered what receptacle a large soup would have arrived in. A baby bath?

"Err, we're not big eaters. If we can't finish it, can we take some away with us?"

"Of course," said the waitress, "I'll bring some containers."

When she had stepped away, I leant towards Fiona.

"We could eat half of this tonight, heat the other half another night, and have two meals for the price of one."

"Great idea," she said, "it's not that expensive either."

The main course would also not have looked out of place at one of the more extravagant Roman orgies; after stuffing ourselves with as much as we could consume without requiring an ambulance, we traipsed down the stairs carrying our bag full of containers and stepped back out into the warm night.

≈ ≈ ≈

"Far out, do these dogs ever have a rest?" asked Fiona as we negotiated a pair copulating on the pavement. Several other dogs barked loudly with encouragement. Two more were conjoined in the middle of the road, oblivious to the odd car driving by. The dogs on one side of the road held a barking competition with the dogs on the other side. It wasn't obvious who'd won, so they had a rematch, followed by a tie-breaker.

As we rounded a corner, harmonious music emanated from the open doors of a church. We peeked inside, and watched a group of Tongans singing, their conductor directing them in a precise graceful mime.

"Choir practice?" I asked.

"I suppose. Nicer noise than the dogs."

Fiona leant on me as she walked.

"How are you feeling?" I asked her.

"Still jetlagged a bit. That enormous meal didn't help. I need to lie down."

We stuffed our left-over Chinese into the fridge at Toni's, and headed to bed.

Bed.

Pillow.

Mmmmmmmmmmmm.

Pause.

"Woof."

Pause.

"Woof woof woof woof woof woof woof woof."

"Gaaah bloody dogs," I said.

This was a warm-up for an alternative choir practice.

"Aaarroooo," it began.

"Aaarrrooooooooooooooooooooooooooooooooo."

"Far out," said Fiona, "this is impossible."

"Aaarrrroooooooooo–oooooooooooo–oooooooooo–oooooooo," sang multiple dogs simultaneously.

We drifted into an inevitable sleep after several hours. The dogs hadn't finished their singing, we'd just become so exhausted, the noise had blended into our dreams.

Dreams.

Sleep.

It was 4 a.m.

I was in the middle of a complicated dream involving riding in a minibus with Claudia holding baby Toni, pursued by several barking dogs.

"Pok?" inquired something outside our window, experimentally.

"Pok pok pok."

Pause.

"Pok pok pok pok pok pok pok pok pok pok."

"Far out," said Fiona again, wrapping her pillow around her ears, "now it's bloody chickens. We'll never get any sleep ever."

"Pok pok pok pok."

"Woof."

Pause.

"Woof woof woof woof woof woof woof woof."

"Pok pok pok pok pok pok pok pok pok pok."

NOOOOOOOOOO!

We fell back to sleep after sunrise, and slept the sleep of the jetlagged, the sleep of the night shift worker, the sleep of people who know there is absolutely nothing at all they need to get out of bed for.

Kesi's voice intruded via my upper ear.

"Simon, Jan from Octopus Diving is here!"

Diving.

I'd completely forgotten I'd arranged diving.

For 9 a.m.

I jumped out of bed, threw on swimmers and a T-shirt and sandals, grabbed my bag of diving gear and exited. Fiona continued snoozing.

≈ ≈ ≈

The promise of a hot day, the excitement of impending outdoor activities; my mood lifted as soon as I stepped outside.

Jan's ancient khaki Land Rover pickup waited in front of Toni's, the engine clattering under the bonnet as if it contained a miniature saucepan factory.

"Throw your bag in the back and climb in," he shouted.

I slammed the car door behind me, and sagged into the ripped seat. Out of habit, I reached over my shoulder for a seatbelt, which was absent.

Jan's rapid acceleration and deceleration, combined with the frequent potholes, made the ride more thrilling than the dodgems at Fletcher's Steam Fair. He changed gear constantly, as if he were stirring a box of bricks.

"Where are you from originally?" I shouted, over the noise of grinding engine parts.

"From Holland. I met a Tongan lady when I was living in New Zealand, and well, here we are. How about you?"

He spoke excellent English.

"I'm going to New Zealand after this. I met a New Zealand lady when I was living in England, and well, here we are."

Jan nodded and gripped the steering wheel with both hands while looking straight ahead.

Did he ever laugh?

At his house, we loaded dive tanks and other equipment into the back of the Land Rover, and drove about 100 metres to the wharf at the end of his street.

I held on to the wooden cabin of his blue-and-white boat to steady myself as I jumped in. Jan passed me the dive equipment and joined me.

"I fixed the engine," he said, "can you untie the boat once I start her?"

I took the rope in my hands in readiness, happy in the importance of my task. A chug-chug-chug-chug began from under the floorboards. I looked at Jan for confirmation, and seeing him nod from the wheelhouse, I released the rope and stepped inside to join him.

"Today," said Jan, "we'll head to Fafa Island, it's an easy dive to start with. How many dives have you done before?"

"I've done about 40. I have my rescue diver certification."

"Have you ever dived in the tropics?"

"No, all my experience is in England, with a bit in the Mediterranean."

"You're in for a treat."

The boat chugged further out to sea.

"Look, flying fish," shouted Jan, pointing. "Still flying, still flying, still flying, and…. plooop."

I covered my mouth and tried not to laugh at the 'plooop'. I hadn't seen the fish though.

"Another one. Still flying, still flying, and…. plooop."

There was a danger I would start giggling, and I didn't want to appear rude. I stared at the sea, so Jan couldn't see my expression. Then I saw one.

"Wow, I always thought flying fish just jumped out of the sea for a bit," I said, "I didn't realise they flew along with little wings; that one was out of the water for half a minute."

"Yes, and then they fall back in… plooop."

Flying fish surrounded the boat. My amazement at seeing them had extinguished my reaction to Jan's expression.

Thank goodness I haven't offended him.

In a few minutes we reached Fafa Island. Jan threw an anchor out, and the chug-chug-chug silenced. Submerged rocks appeared through deep blue-green ocean.

We kitted up and sat on the side of the boat, our backs to the water.

"Ready?" asked Jan.

"Ready."

Our air regulators in our mouths, we fell backwards, and upon landing I gave Jan the 'okay' sign, a thumb and forefinger circle. As we sank through the warm water, the corals, the colourful fish, the shapes of the rocks all entranced me. This was such an improvement on diving the Mediterranean.

Jan grabbed my arm and pointed. I couldn't work out what he was showing me, and I shrugged. He made a movement with his hand simulating a single horn on his forehead, then pointed again. I understood what he was indicating. A fish with one horn. He made the movement again. A unicorn fish! There was a greater variety of life here than in a David Attenborough documentary.

After 30 minutes we surfaced.

"Did you enjoy that?" said Jan.

"Loved it. Where to next?"

"We can go back via Makaha'a reef. There's a lot of organ coral."

We climbed on board. Jan started the engine again and raised the anchor. I realised with sadness we'd destroyed some coral formations in the process of dropping it.

Makaha'a reef appeared under us, an immense field of coral resembling the tops of organ pipes, as if someone had scuttled a piece of Westminster Abbey. Little colourful fish swam amongst them, darting between the formations. I wished Fiona was with me to share the experience.

≈ ≈ ≈

Jan dropped me back at Toni's Guest House. A tummy earthquake of roughly 6.4 on the Richter scale reminded me that I hadn't eaten yet that day.

Fiona relaxed in the green outdoor seating area, reading a book entitled *The Happy Isles of Oceania*, by a certain Paul Theroux.

"Hiya Simon, did you have a good time?" she asked. "Toni has a little library here, I found this book. It's got a chapter about Tonga, I find it pretty depressing though."

"Yes, Paul Theroux came across a bit miserable from memory. Let's eat brunch, I'm starving."

"I've already been to the supermarket. It's called Morris Hedstrom, and it stocks most provisions. Have a look at what I bought."

She opened the kitchen cupboard and fridge, and pulled out some fresh bread, margarine, jam, fruit, and a box with *Sanitarium* advertised on the side.

"What the hell is Sanitarium?" I asked, "it sounds like the name of a mental institution."

Fiona laughed. "It's a brand of New Zealand cereal. Most of the packaged foods here seem to come from New Zealand. It's a bit like coming home for me."

I inspected the box of Sanitarium.

"Fiona, it's out of date. Only by a month, but still.."

"I know. A lot of the packets in the shops are. I reckon the Tongans receive food shipped here that New Zealand supermarkets can't sell. I'm sure it'll be fine."

Over brunch I shared my morning diving stories, and promised I'd take her snorkelling one day, so she could share the experience.

"Apart from grocery shopping," I asked, "what have you been up to while I was out?"

"I sat and read for a bit. Anja and Claudia were doing something in the kitchen, but they didn't speak to me. Oh, and a man came round selling tickets to a native dancing show at the Tongan National Centre tonight. I bought two."

"That was the evening entertainment Isy back in Hawaii and Tomasi both mentioned," I said. "I'm not sure it'll be authentic. D'you feel comfortable watching these local people dress up, and do their tribal rituals for paying tourists like they're performing puppets?"

"The tickets weren't expensive, and they include a traditional meal. Give it a chance, you might enjoy it. You liked the Hawaiian Luau."

Does the traditional meal mean burger and chips?

"All right," I said, "I guess the Chinese leftovers will have to wait for tomorrow."

Toni entered the kitchen, the smell of hand-rolled tobacco preceding him by five seconds.

"Hello, you guys. Have you had much of a chance to see anything yet?"

"Yep," I said, "we've seen some of Nuku'alofa, and I've been on a dive trip to Fafa island."

"Did you go with Jan? He's a serious chap, isn't he? Good operator though. So, you've seen some of the town? How would you like to tour the entire Tongatapu island next week? I'm running a bit of a day trip on Monday. There's space in the bus if you want to come."

"Yes please, Toni, sounds great," said Fiona.

"What should we bring with us?" I asked.

Toni hand-rolled a cigarette as he continued. He already possessed an unsmoked one behind his left ear. "Swimmers and a towel, a camera of course, and some money to buy lunch. It's one hundred pa'anga each for the tour. You can pay me on Monday. See you at nine."

He stuffed the cigarette in the corner of his mouth and departed, leaving the tobacco aroma behind him.

"Sounds great, doesn't it Simon? We'll see loads."

"It does. I need a nap now though, the heat and the broken sleep last night are getting to me."

We lay down and Fiona read about our evening destination from our guidebook. "The Tongan National Centre provides residents and visitors alike with the opportunity to see demonstrations of traditional handicrafts, taste the delicious food and join in a famous *kava* ceremony. Do not miss the guitar playing and native dancing."

"That sounds contrived," I said, closing my eyes. "The kava bit should be interesting though, kava's supposed to be hallucinogenic. At least we'll find out what they eat in Tonga, apart from burgers and Chinese."

≈ ≈ ≈

The daytime ferocity of the sun had diminished, as we took a cold shower and dressed for the evening. An afternoon siesta could easily become a daily event, despite the sweat.

We were sitting in the communal area when Kesi called out, "Simon, Fiona, the Tongan National Centre bus is here."

A slimmer version of Isy from Hawaii opened the sliding door at the side of a minibus. As we hopped in, I read the centre's logo embroidered on his brown shirt. The bus had already collected an older couple from their accommodation, but we'd no time to exchange any greeting apart from a nod and a smile, as two minutes later we arrived at our destination.

"Welcome," said mini-Isy, "to the Tongan National Centre."

He helped us out and gestured we should enter the building. I gathered he'd also be our guide.

"Good evening," he addressed us, as we congregated inside the door, "my name is Siaosi."

Too late. I'm already naming you mini-Isy.

"Before our show tonight, please enjoy the exhibits in our museum. There'll be an announcement when dinner is ready. This way please."

A side room contained multiple artefacts of Tongan history. We regarded a large model of a dugout canoe sailing elegantly across a concrete sea. Paintings and vast sheets of *tapa* cloth hung on the walls. The description informed us that ladies beating plant fibres manufactured the cloths by hand, and some of them dated from the 1800s.

A collection of sepia photographs distracted me. I began searching for Queen Sālote among the subjects, when Fiona called me over.

The remains of an animal displayed in a glass case had attracted her attention. In a previous existence, it looked like it had been a tortoise.

"What have you found, Fiona? I didn't know tortoises lived in Tonga?"

17.
Disco and Religion

Fiona summarised the description of the tortoise.

"This chappie was the only one. He died in 1966 at almost 200 years old."

"Amazing," I said. "But what was he doing in Tonga?"

"Believe it or not, Captain Cook gave him to the King of Tonga in 1777, a monarch named *Fa-ta-fe-hi Pa-u-la-ho*." She read the name carefully, syllable by syllable. "The king bestowed a royal title on the tortoise, it attended kava ceremonies, and loved to wander around the palace."

"But where did Captain Cook find the tortoise?"

"Probably the Galapagos, or some other islands he'd visited on the way to Tonga. Poor Tortoise. 200 years and it was all alone with no other tortoises to talk to."

Fiona regarded the empty shell sadly.

I put my arm round her. "Come on, let's see what else is here."

The final exhibit was an enormous floor-standing cooking pot. It was about a metre across and a metre tall. It was well weather-beaten, and had a chunk missing from its side.

The older couple from our bus were examining it as we approached.

"What do you imagine they cooked in that, Derek?"

Derek started to answer and was cut off by his wife's next question.

"Do you imagine it was so large because Tongans have big families, Derek?"

"I think…," said Derek and was again interrupted.

"It must have taken a long time to heat food in it, don't you reckon, Derek?"

I realised Derek was a man who'd never been permitted to finish a sentence.

Fiona piped up. "I believe they cooked people in it. The Tongans were cannibals a long time ago, until the missionaries persuaded them to stop."

"That's it," said Derek, wisely curtailing his sentence at two words.

"People?" said his wife. "People? Why would they cook people? Were they short of food, Derek?"

"I don't…," began Derek, unsuccessfully.

Fiona and I left them to a conversation that had clearly been continuing in this vein for decades. We'd heard guitar music starting in the next room.

We sat down at a round dining table laid for six people, facing a stage on which two men playing guitars, and a third playing a ukulele, sang Pacific music into microphones. A backdrop of a vast tapa cloth covered the entire wall. The heat, the music, the slow rotation of the ceiling fans above us, it was all very relaxing.

I leant back in my chair and closed my eyes, listening to the singing.

"Derek, let's sit here with this nice young couple. Nobody sitting here are they?"

We indicated the seats were indeed available.

Mini-Isy approached us. "Please, help yourselves from the buffet." He gestured toward a table piled with sliced pork, chicken, vegetables, yams, bread, and fresh tropical fruits for dessert. We took a little of everything and returned to our table.

"Fiona, I don't feel comfortable with this, many Tongans would never see this amount of food. I'm a bit embarrassed eating this in front of them."

"They do this show every week. They'll have seen this before, don't worry."

Derek and his wife returned from the buffet.

"Why did you pick up pineapple, Derek? You don't like pineapple."

"Well, I…,"

"Remember that time in Australia you had pineapple? You were sick."

"I was?"

"Ah look," I said, hoping to save Derek from another verbal battering, "the show's about to start."

The music gained momentum and male and female dancers appeared on stage. The mens' long pink and blue grass skirts swayed as the wooden poles they carried next to their shiny oiled chests thumped on the floor.

White pointy headdresses topped the ladies' red and brown corsets and long skirts. Their short wooden clubs clonked together.

One of the young muscly male dancers caught Fiona's eye.

"He's rather attractive," she said, temporarily losing interest in her tropical fruit.

Derek was clapping and enjoying the dancing far too much for his wife's approval. I hoped her glare wouldn't turn him to stone in front of us.

The music and dancing lasted around fifteen minutes. Despite my earlier misgivings, I enjoyed it, and I realised this was a way for the Tongans to make some money from us wealthy *palangis*.

A wooden bowl containing kava, the hallucinogenic liquid the colour of dirty washing-up water, began its journey around the audience. It arrived at our table, and I took a small sip from the coconut shell offered, nervous about the reported after-effects.

It tasted like dirty washing-up water.

"What's that supposed to do?" I asked Fiona, wiping my mouth with the back of my hand.

"No idea." She sipped some and grimaced. "It does nothing for me."

Derek took the shell from Fiona. His wife confiscated it before he could try any.

"Don't have any of that, Derek, you don't know where it's been."

I thought of replying indignantly the last person to touch it had been my girlfriend, but I stopped myself, realising this was a woman who'd never lost an argument in her life.

The dancing finished, and mini-Isy approached us once more. "The evening's entertainment is over. Please have a browse of our gift shop before you leave."

"Gift shop?" asked Fiona, getting up. "Come on, Simon."

The shop contained a few books about Tonga, a couple of souvenirs and some postcards. We bought a miniature kava bowl, which we reckoned would be a good talking point on a dining room table in some future life, and a few cards. As it seemed mini-Isy's responsibilities didn't extend to driving us home, we left.

Outside we found the dancers, chatting in the light of the centre windows. They had changed out of their grass skirts and headdresses. The young man Fiona had found so attractive greeted me.

"Hallo," he said, "did you enjoy the show?"

"We did, thank you, your dancing was great."

Fiona slid behind me and looked down at her feet. I could sense her blushing even though it was dark.

"Where are you staying?" the dancer asked me.

"We're at Toni's Guest House."

"That's on my way, would you like a lift?"

"Thank you, that'd be wonderful."

We climbed into his old Toyota, and rode back to Toni's with him. I asked him what effect the kava should have.

"They water the kava down at the show. A real kava ceremony takes several hours. You need to drink quite a bit of kava for it to have any impact."

≈ ≈ ≈

The sound of chirping insects, barking dogs, and thumping bass drums welcomed us as we climbed out of the dancer's car, and stood in the dim exterior light of Toni's Guest House.

"Sleep's going to be impossible tonight," I said, "It's boiling hot, the dogs are in full song, and just listen to that Saturday night disco."

"Yep, no idea how we're going to block out that noise, the music's right across the street."

"Well, we don't have to get up for anything tomorrow. Let's find some books in Toni's collection, and read them on the bed. Maybe it'll stop soon."

"Good idea. I want to dip into some more of Paul Theroux' adventures."

The little library in the deserted living room contained thirty dog-eared paperbacks. Travellers had swapped their finished books for unread ones, and most of them were in German, Dutch or French.

Fiona pulled out *The Happy Isles of Oceania* again.

I ran my finger along the books on offer.

Maybe I should improve my French?

Gustave Flaubert's *Madame Bovary* glared at me accusingly from the shelf. I had studied it at school, hated it, and despite leaving it unfinished had scraped a pass. Nope. That'd be literary flagellation, why the hell would any young backpacker be travelling with this tome of torture? Relaxation required something in English.

Forced to choose between *Lovers and Gamblers* by Jackie Collins, an Agatha Christie called *Hercule Poirot's Christmas*, and *Travels* by Michael Crichton, I chose *Travels* as I had no appetite for chick-lit or murder mystery.

To the background of Boney M explaining what they'd accomplished by a river in Babylon, we lay on the bed in our underwear and opened our books.

Fiona read me passages about Paul Theroux kayaking around the Pacific islands. He'd reached some impressively remote parts, but I found his opinions of the country and the locals rather negative. In Nuku'alofa we'd experienced nothing but positive experiences. I hoped his report wasn't representative of the smaller islands we were travelling to.

I had already read Michael Crichton's *Jurassic Park*, so I dipped into *Travels*. The two books were completely different. *Travels* didn't contain any dinosaurs. It was a collection of short stories, journeys through his mind as well as physical locations, some of it was plain weird. His descriptions of Thailand and Africa enthralled me, and I was in the middle of his bizarre experience of sitting in an American desert, learning psychology from a cactus, when Fiona interrupted me.

"Listen," she said.

"What?"

"The music's stopped. Everything's gone quiet."

"What time is it?"

"Midnight. Bang on. Must be nightclub closing time. That's early, in London they don't close until 3 a.m."

"You know why, Fiona, it's Sunday now. Remember what that Tongan musician, Tomasi, told me at the airport? On Sunday, no-one may do anything in Tonga except go to church. The rule must start exactly at midnight."

"What happens if you need food, or you have to go to hospital?"

"I'm sure there's an exception for medical emergencies, but Tomasi told me on Sunday all the shops are closed, and you're not allowed to play sport, dig the garden, or even drive a car."

"Wow," said Fiona, discarding Paul Theroux and dropping him unceremoniously on the floor, "it's a shame nobody's informed the dogs of this curfew."

We went to sleep to the sound of enthusiastic canine discussion.

≈ ≈ ≈

I lay motionless on my back. The early bright sunshine had a definite Sunday morning feel. Apart from the continual animal noises, at 7 a.m. it was quiet. No cars, no people's voices.

I watched Fiona sleep, her rug of red hair decorating the pillow.

She's such a perfect travelling companion, what adventures will we have today?

Michael Crichton lay beside me on the floor, and I picked him up and randomly selected another chapter. He had an interest in the occult, and I read fascinating tales about flying on the astral plane, past lives, and something called an entity. I was enjoying the peace. Fiona turned over in her sleep.

At 8 a.m. flawless harmonic singing commenced from at least two different directions.

Fiona opened her eyes, sat up and stretched her arms.

"Who's singing at this time in the morning?" she asked.

"I think it's the church services starting. We should probably go to one; there's nothing else open today. I passed some churches on the way to the dive shop."

"All right, let's have breakfast and go for a stroll."

≈ ≈ ≈

Ten o'clock found us at the bottom of a huge sweeping staircase surrounded by lush tropical gardens, the entrance to the Basilica of Saint Anthony of Padua. We weren't catholic, but we chose Saint Anthony's as it was the biggest church in the city, with a vast conical tin roof.

Fiona was most irreverent. "This is the first time I've been to church in a circus tent."

"Sssh, don't let anyone hear you say that. They take their religion seriously here. Come on, let's go inside, it'll be starting."

The service had begun as we ascended the stairs, and we stood at the back, too late to sit down. We peered round the edges of the huge Tongans standing in front of us, unable to see the front of the church.

The first hymn started, a rousing, upbeat number. I recognised the tune, although the words were in Tongan. Singing in English churches was a hit-and-miss affair, with the most off-key voices belting out the loudest offerings. Here it was different.

Every member of the congregation sang in tune, the harmonies rising and falling as if they'd all been practising together. I didn't dare join in. Even if Tongan had been my native tongue, my untrained voice would have spoiled the whole hymn.

The architecture fascinated me. This church had been designed by a Tongan Sir Christopher Wren, the wooden beams soared into the apex of the cone, and light filtered through small windows around the edge.

After the service had ended, an older Tongan man noticed us studying the building and approached. He spoke in a deep voice, his tones like those a cave might have if it could speak.

"Good morning. I am Tukupa. Welcome to our church. Are you visiting Tonga for long?"

"Simon and Fiona," I said. "We're here for a few weeks and then travelling on to New Zealand."

"Wonderful. What are you planning on doing while you're in Nuku'alofa?"

"Well, I'm here on a bit of a quest. I've decided I want to see the Queen of Tonga, like my father did in the 1950s, in London. Of course, I know it's a different queen now."

Tukupa's elderly face smiled, but it was an expression of commiseration.

"The queen your father would have seen was Queen Sālote. She died in 1965. I was a pallbearer at her funeral."

"You carried her coffin?" I asked.

"I did, along with 107 other men. We bore her a quarter of a mile to the Royal Tombs. It was my greatest honour. The massed Tongan bands played *The Funeral March*, the army and 50,000 people attended, together with the leaders of other Pacific Island nations, Fiji, Samoa, New Zealand. We all loved her so dearly."

He paused, and he reminded me of my own father reminiscing on his encounter with this grand lady.

Tukupa brightened. "Anyway, Queen Havaevalu is our queen now."

I thought back to our research at the library in London.

Havaevalu. That's what they call her for short.

Tukupa raised one finger flat against his mouth.

"There is something here I would like to show you. Come."

18.
Dooof

Tukupa led us through the pews, to the opposite side of the church. The smell of incense pervaded the stuffy air. I hoped it wouldn't exacerbate Fiona's asthma.

He indicated artefacts as we passed, stopping at one vivid three-dimensional montage. "This is station eleven of the cross," he said, "where our dear Lord was stripped of his garments. Study his hair. What do you see?"

We searched Jesus's hair as respectfully as we could. I didn't want anyone to think I was looking for nits.

Fiona spotted it first. "There's a tiny jewel in his hair. Is it a palm tree? What's that for?"

"Well done, young lady, said Tukupa. "You are very observant. The little golden coconut tree belonged to Queen Sālote, the queen at the coronation in London, and whose coffin I carried. I can't remember how it came to be here, but it has her royal history."

I admired the gold tree.

One of Queen Sālote's possessions. A connection to her.

I wanted to take a photo, but didn't think I should inside the church.

"Thank you for showing us this, Tukupa," I said. "It's special."

"Queen Sālote's grave is in the royal tombs, opposite our church. You could visit it, and the palace is nearby too, but I'm not sure the royal couple are here now."

He bowed slightly, and I found myself copying him.

"Thank you again for visiting our church."

"Tukupa, it was an absolute honour to meet you."

I meant it. I had never expected to converse with one of Queen Sālote's pallbearers.

On the way out, I put some money into the offertory box, in memory of my father's favourite monarch.

≈ ≈ ≈

A rusty fence and gate which we couldn't penetrate surrounded the royal tombs, and five immense worn-down statues guarded them. Three represented monarchs interred there, and one was of a lion. The fifth monument stood in the centre of the others. Discolouration ran down their weathered once-white stone steps and small trees grew out of them. I was glad we were there during the day. At night it must have resembled the set of Michael Jackson's *Thriller.*

We stood respectfully looking at the tombs.

"This place is depressing," said Fiona. "It gives me the creeps. Can we leave? Let's find the royal palace. Maybe their royal highnesses will be home."

"All right. It is rather eerie."

Goodbye, Queen Sālote. My father sends his regards and fond memories.

An avenue led to the palace, which commanded a view over the sea. It was the largest wooden building I had ever seen.

I pulled out our guidebook.

"Listen to this. This palace was constructed in New Zealand and brought here in 1867. How did they transport such an immense building?"

"I've seen houses chopped in half being driven along New Zealand roads on the backs of trucks," said Fiona. "They probably did that with the palace, only it would have been horses and carts, and they must have chopped it into quarters. Maybe tenths."

"It doesn't seem occupied. There's no-one around, not even guards. It's amazing to stand this close to it. I mean, Buckingham Palace has all those railings and policemen."

"It looks unloved, all shut up like this. It'd be better to see it when the king and queen are in residence."

We left the abandoned palace and strolled back to Toni's.

≈ ≈ ≈

We wanted to hold hands, but our skin squelched together with sweat, plus we weren't sure whether we should show displays of affection on Sundays. Heat-exhausted, our steps were slow, one foot in front of the other. It was past lunchtime; the heat suppressed any hunger.

There was one thing to do on this Sunday afternoon—siesta.

We lay on top of the sheets for several hours, craving air conditioning or a fan, and dozed.

I woke up in a pool of sweat bigger and saltier than the Dead Sea. Fiona was reading her book, lying on her tummy propped up on her elbows.

"How are you feeling, Fiona?"

"I'm hot and yuck. I need three showers a day here."

"What's for dinner tonight?"

"Left-over Chinese."

"Of course, I forgot we had that. Yum. Let's eat."

We had the kitchen to ourselves. Fiona pulled the Chinese food out of the communal fridge. There was such an enormous amount, we split it into two.

Fiona pushed some buttons. "How does this microwave work? It doesn't matter what I press, nothing happens."

"Let me have a look. Okay, power setting max. How long do you think we need to cook it for?"

"Try two minutes to start?"

"I'm pressing two, zero, zero, start. It says *error*."

"What does 'error' mean?"

"Should we enter the time first, before the power level? I'll try that. Okay here we go, it's working."

The food rotated inside the microwave. Fiona pulled some cutlery out of a drawer, and put it on a table. She found two glasses, rinsed them out, filled them with bottled water and set them down.

"This is homely, isn't it?" she said.

"I was just thinking we were being most domesticated."

BANG!

"Quick, stop the bloody microwave. Press the 'door open' button."

Fiona pressed it, and the door swung outwards. Chinese food covered the inside of the microwave, the sides, the glass door, the top.

"Dinner," said Fiona, "is served."

We scraped up as much as we could, and shared it between two plates.

"It's a good job there was such a lot to begin with," I said.

"I think this cooking lark is overrated," said Fiona. "I propose we eat out from now on."

We finished our food, cleaned the microwave, and washed our dishes.

Back in our room, we lay down and carried on reading the books we'd found.

Michael Crichton's book fascinated me. I hoped I could finish it before we had to leave. I wanted to visit all the places he was describing.

The sounds of distant choirs at evening church services was a welcome backdrop. Even the dog and chicken noises had blended into the generic noises of the night.

The heat and humidity were still stifling well after dark, and we fell into an uneasy sleep.

Choirs.

Heavenly music.

Heaven.

Sleep.

DOOOF DOOOF DOOOF DOOOF DOOOF

Fiona sat up. "Far out, what the hell is that?"

"No idea. What time is it?"

Fiona found her watch. "It's just after midnight."

"You know what I reckon? The nightclubs are starting up again. It's technically not Sunday any more."

"So, they pressed pause for 24 hours during Sunday, went to church, said their prayers, sang their hymns, and now everyone starts partying again? Wow. Just wow."

We lay in bed listening to the dooof, which continued until the early hours.

≈ ≈ ≈

It was 9 a.m.

Again.

Sergeant-Major Kesi's voice woke us for early morning reveille. "Simon, Fiona! Toni's island tour is leaving now."

We fell out of bed into another hot and sunny day and grabbed a quick piece of bread and jam. One other traveller joined us for the tour; a girl in her early twenties. An expensive camera hung around her neck, the straps hidden under her shoulder-length curly black hair.

Toni took some time rolling himself a cigarette and then introduced himself to the new arrival.

"I'm Toni. How long are you staying with us?"

"Hi, I'm Bronwyn. I'm here for a week."

"You're not even here long enough to slow down to Tongan time. Where are you from?" Toni asked.

"New Zealand. The North Island."

"I've been there," said Toni, "I spent three hours in Auckland airport, so I've seen New Zealand."

Both Bronwyn and Fiona looked unimpressed with this sentiment.

Toni escorted us to his ancient vehicle, and we all climbed through the sliding door into the back. Toni hopped into the driver's seat, his unlit cigarette placed on the dashboard.

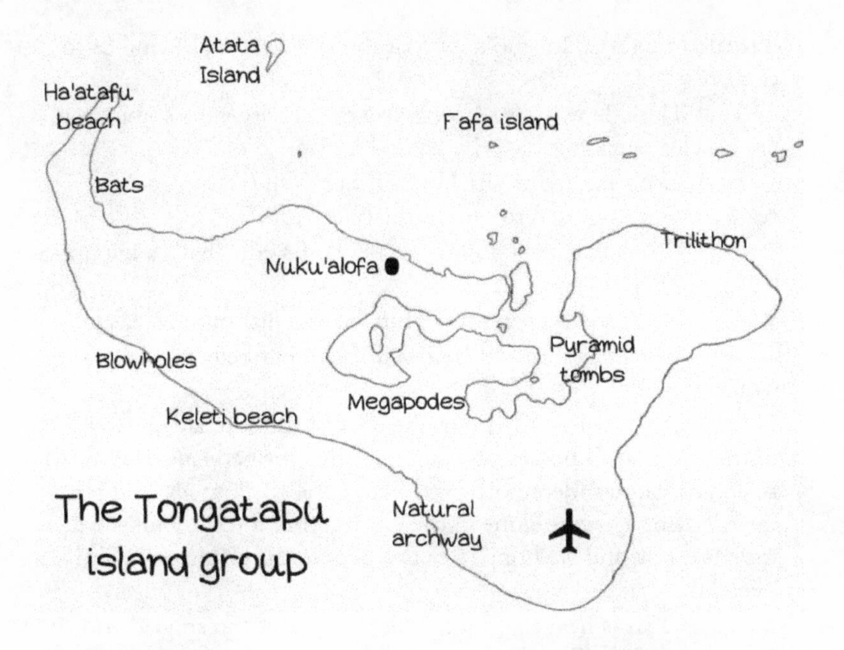

"Which part of New Zealand's North Island are you from?" Fiona asked Bronwyn. "I'm from the West Coast of the South Island."

"Wow, I'm from Hamilton. I've been living in London for two years though."

"Me too. And I'm bringing an Englishman home." Fiona introduced me.

The minibus coughed up several portions of phlegm before settling into a rhythmic rattle, and we moved off at the customary lethargic pace. I recognised we were heading away from Nuku'alofa on the road back toward the airport, then we turned down an unsealed track, its edges thick with lush green foliage. The bus lurched from side to side as we proceeded, abseiling down mineshaft sized potholes, then ascending the opposite inclines. Fiona looked sick, and I hoped the entire trip wouldn't be on bumpy roads.

After a few minutes of this treatment, we burst out of the jungle and faced a stunning view of the sea.

"Here we are at Keleti beach." announced Toni. "If the tide's in, you'll be able to go for a swim." He exited the bus and retreated to a rock to smoke two or three cigarettes, leaving us to explore.

The tide was out. A long way out. There were some deep, crystal clear rock pools, so Fiona and I stripped off.

Fiona paused as she took off her T-shirt. "I've just realised, I've forgotten to put on my bikini top."

"Well, you can't go topless here," I said, "that's a big no-no in Tonga."

"I'll have to keep my T-shirt on and just put my legs in."

Fiona's T-shirt finished well above her belly button, so it would stay dry.

Despite the early hour, the heat of the sun had already warmed the small bodies of water and they formed natural jacuzzis. Bronwyn had wandered off to paddle in the shallow sea, and for the moment we were alone in the pools. After a few minutes we were too hot, and we hopped out and lay in the shade of a palm tree.

"This is heaven," Fiona said, "I love it. I'm so glad you brought me here."

Toni stood over us, grinning. "No time for lazing around, on to the next stop."

After a brief wait for Bronwyn, who'd disappeared, we piled back into the bus.

"Sorry, sorry," said Bronwyn, "I had to take some photos. This place is amazing."

"What's next, tour leader?" I asked.

"We're going to visit a very unusual native animal," said Toni.

The bus trundled carefully back up the track. This time we knew what to expect, although at one pothole Bronwyn was concentrating on changing her film, and was tipped on to the floor in a heap of camera straps and film containers.

"Sorry," called Toni, "best to hold on tight."

I helped her into her seat. Where the jungle track re-joined the main road, we pulled into a small car park.

"This," said Toni, mysteriously, "is the home of the *Niuafo'ou Megapode.*"

19.
Stonehenge and The Pyramids

None of us had any idea what kind of animal a Niuafo'ou Megapode was, whether it waddled or flew, and most importantly, whether its primary food source consisted of young backpackers. We entered the reception area, where a European lady stood behind the counter.

"Welcome to the Brehm Fund Bird Park," she said, "I will give you a small tour."

The Niuafo'ou Megapode, we discovered, is a highly endangered bird, the last remaining type of a previously widespread species. It owes its survival to the tiny islands it lives on, which are inaccessible to humans. Fiona reminded me these were part of the same group of islands we'd decided against visiting, as the irregular plane schedule might leave us stranded.

We learnt the unique characteristic of these birds is that they create burrows in the ground two metres deep, right above volcanic steam vents. They lay their massive eggs in these holes, which self-incubate in the steam. When the chicks hatch, they dig their way through the earth to the surface, where their first experience of life is to be attacked by giant ants.

The Megapodes are almost extinct, and the Brehm Fund Bird Park is trying to reintroduce them to a wider selection of islands, so the remaining population is diverse and able to withstand catastrophe.

We gave generously to the park's work. I reckoned anyone being born with a volcano up their bum needed the best chance at life.

≈ ≈ ≈

The minibus continued its gradual journey, further along the airport road. We stopped at the Hufangalupe natural archway, where dramatic seas crashed at the bottom of high cliffs.

Toni sat next to the bus again, rolling a cigarette. This tour wasn't anything new to him.

"This view is a great contender for a photography prize," said Bronwyn. "Which do you reckon is the best angle?"

We walked with her close to the edge, and looked down into the homicidal sea a thousand miles below us.

"You wouldn't want to fall in there," I said.

"Can you hold on to me?" she asked, "I want to lean over and take some photos."

Before we could stop her, she lay down on the edge of the cliff. Fiona grabbed hold of her legs, and I grabbed hold of Fiona. Bronwyn was leaning right out, snapping away.

"Pull me back," she shouted, and we dragged her across the grass.

"You're really into photography, aren't you?" said Fiona.

"I love it, I've even won a few small prizes. It's a bit expensive though, as I use a hell of a lot of film, and I have to ration it. I've only brought ten more 36's to last until New Zealand. I'm not sure if you can even buy it here. It'll be fantastic when digital cameras become more available."

"Digital cameras?" I asked, "what are they?"

"They're a camera that plugs straight into a computer. Casio and Kodak make them, and I was undecided about buying one in London, but the picture quality isn't nearly as good as film. I'll hold off for a while, I think. They're bound to come down in price as well."

We found Toni, and the bus set off again. This time the journey was longer, following the coast.

"Has anyone here seen Stonehenge?" asked Toni, in his tour guide voice.

We all said we'd seen Stonehenge.

"I bet you didn't know Tonga has Stonehenge too."

We admitted that until now our education had disregarded this fact.

"We're headed for Heketa," said Toni. "Hundreds of years ago, it was the capital of Tonga, and there are some old constructions, like Stonehenge. Tongans consider it to be a sacred site."

We arrived at Heketa and climbed out of the bus. Toni looked at Fiona's T-shirt, fashionably cropped short and finishing halfway down her tummy.

"I don't suppose you could cover up a bit," he said. "The Tongans don't appreciate seeing belly buttons here. What happened to your T-shirt? Did you run out of material?"

He laughed at his own joke.

"I don't have anything else with me," said Fiona.

"There's a sarong in my bag," said Bronwyn, "you could borrow it while we're here."

Fiona wrapped the sarong round her middle and legs in the fashion of a long dress, which passed Toni's inspection.

Fiona read from our guidebook. "The Ha'amonga'a Trilithon, 'The Burden of Maui', comprises two huge standing stones, about three times as tall as a human, with a third lintel stone resting across the top of them."

It did, indeed, resemble a section of Stonehenge.

Fiona continued reading from the guide. "The Trilithon was probably built in the 13th Century, by the King Tu'itatui. The theory was the Trilithon formed the entrance to the Royal compound, when Heketa was the capital of Tonga. In the 1960s, the current King Tupou IV studied a design carved into the lintel and believed it may have been connected to predicting seasons. He ordered the forests around the Trilithon be cleared and on the following winter solstice in 1967, he stood here and observed the sun rose and set in exact alignment with two of the lines on the design. Six months later the study was repeated for the summer solstice, and the corresponding lines were likewise accurate."

"Isn't that amazing?" I said, "the ancient Tongans were astronomers, like the druids of old England?"

Bronwyn snapped multiple pictures. "Wait until I show my folks this. Dad's always wanted to see Stonehenge, but he doesn't think he could manage the flight to England; he might come here though."

We walked on and arrived at a single vast lump of stone. Fiona posed in front of it. It was twice as tall as her and four times wider.

She consulted the guidebook. "This was the king's backrest."

"I know some Tongans are pretty big," I said, "but this guy must have won first prize in the local meaty majesty competition."

"It says here it was a primitive throne," said Fiona. "The king would lean against this when threatened by assassins, and it defended him against approach from behind."

We stared at the backrest. Bronwyn took some more pictures.

I couldn't work out how the early Tongans had moved this vast monolith here. It was an extraordinary accomplishment.

Fresh water melon from a vendor at the Trilithon dribbled down our chins and made our hands sticky as we returned to the bus and set off once more.

"Has anyone here seen the pyramids in Egypt?" asked Toni.

Fiona and Bronwyn both stated they had.

"Tonga has pyramids too." Toni paused, waiting for a surprised expression from his customers.

I had this vision of teams of hundreds of rotund Tongans hauling blocks of stone through the jungle, supervised by a gigantic doughnut munching monarch. It seemed impossible, but I had seen what they could achieve with the Trilithon.

A huge stone platform, as big as a tennis court, and partly covered in jungle, dwarfed Toni's bus as he parked beside it. Toni perched on the side of it to roll another cigarette.

"It's a bit short for a pyramid," I said, "were there more layers once?"

Fiona again read from the guide. "The *Langi* or 'Pyramid tombs' contain the bodies of Tongan Royalty. In total there are 28 royal stone tombs, 15 of which are enormous. This largest tomb probably houses the body of Tele'a', a king who reigned in the 16th century, although it may only be a memorial to him, as legend says he was lost at sea."

"This is incredible," I said. "Just think, Queen Sālote's ancestors. The history, it's amazing."

The bus drove a short distance while we ate some more fruit, then stopped again. Toni pointed out of the bus window.

"You see that tree?" he said.

"Which one?" we all asked.

"The stumpy one."

"Which stumpy one?"

"Never mind. This is the spot where Captain Cook first landed in Tonga, in 1777. He had a sleep under that tree."

The barrel of tourist attractions was being well scraped.

"Any chance we could copy him?" asked Fiona, "I could do with an after-lunch nap."

We all laughed.

"Let's keep going," said Toni, "there's still a lot to see."

The next stop was some distance away, and we drove for a while through the jungle. Small plantations replaced cleared native trees. We parked at the side of the road near the sea.

"Mapu'a Vaca blowholes," announced Toni. "We've arrived an hour or two before high tide by the looks of it. Perfect."

We walked to the edge of the sea while Toni rolled another cigarette. Flat terraces of rock lined the water's edge, and the waves were breaking dramatically. Each time a wave hit the terraces, fountains of water shot into the air from small cracks in the rock called 'blowholes'. None of us had ever seen anything like this.

"Come on," said Bronwyn, "let's do some photos. I want to take one of you two with a blowhole actually blowing."

Great.

Actually blowing.

We were going to drown.

Bronwyn channelled her inner Steven Spielberg.

"That was a huge one. Simon, could you stand there, and Fiona, just there, next time it goes off it'll be right between you. I'll put the camera on the right setting."

Bronwyn fiddled with the knobs on her camera. Meanwhile, a different blowhole decided to erupt behind Fiona. Bronwyn snapped, missing the best bit of the action.

"Uh-oh, that's the last picture in the film. Wait a sec while I change it."

She turned away. The original blowhole felt it was time to explode. It shot a stream of water about 30 metres into the air, which in slow motion stopped, returned to earth, and splatted over a large area. We took ineffective cover behind our arms, and Fiona received the worst of it. Her hair hung in rats tails over her face.

She shook herself all over like a dog after its bath. She no longer resembled the film star Steven Spielberg needed her to be.

"Damn, damn, damn, sorry, sorry," said Bronwyn, seeing what had happened. "Almost done. Right, let's try again."

Fiona was becoming tired of posing, but like every famous model, she made sacrifices in the name of her art.

"Third time lucky," said Bronwyn, "ready?"

We agreed we were ready.

Nothing happened.

Nothing continued to happen.

"Have you heard of the 'seventh wave' theory?" I said, "I think we may have to wait for the next big one."

We waited.

More nothing happened. Bronwyn held the camera in front of her face, poised, determined not to miss the action.

We waited some more.

20.
Chambo

Bronwyn lowered the camera briefly.

"Don't miss it again," shouted Fiona, more because she wanted to dry off, than out of concern for Bronwyn's competition entries.

The blowhole erupted. Bronwyn snapped four quick pictures.

"I hope that worked, I'll be disappointed if I develop the film and it didn't." She looked at us hopefully. "Should we try one more?"

Toni reappeared. "Ready to move on?" he asked, laughing at the scene in front of him.

We were never more ready.

Fiona and I grabbed our towels and dried our clothes as best we could. Bronwyn looked back at the blowholes.

We climbed in the minibus, and Fiona asked Toni what the next attraction would be.

"Teddy bears," he said, "hanging upside down from trees."

"O…kay…."

I had this vision of some weird, contrived attraction where Tongans took their old teddies to an aerial graveyard and abandoned them in an offering to a celestial Winnie-the-Pooh. Toni didn't expand further, so we munched our fruit and wriggled our bottoms on the seat in our wet swimmers.

"Thanks for being my stars," said Bronwyn. "Sorry about the soaking, I'll buy you both a beer."

"It's okay, Bronwyn," I said, "it's all part of the experience."

Fiona formed a respectable puddle on the floor which, as we trundled round a corner, ran into the door well and disappeared through a crack in the side of the bus.

We arrived at the next stop.

"Look in the trees," said Toni.

We gazed upward. Something was in the treetops. Hundreds of folded umbrellas hung upside down.

"Yuck," said Fiona. "Bats."

They were indeed bats. The flying fox colony of Kolovai, who all had the cutest round faces resembling furry golden teddy bears.

"Aren't they gorgeous?" Bronwyn removed a long camera lens from her bag and fitted it. She snapped about ten pictures of the teddy bears.

"Do they do anything else?" asked Fiona.

"Yes," I said, "at noon every day they all wake up and perform a synchronised dance for the tourists."

"Very funny, Simon."

"They probably sleep until night," I said. "I reckon if you came here at dusk they'd be flying around."

We regarded the sleeping bats. Bronwyn took another picture. They weren't going to do anything more exciting, so we returned to the bus.

"Last stop coming up," announced Toni.

We arrived at Ha'atafu beach, where there was a small resort with a deck and a bar.

"You can borrow snorkelling equipment here," said Toni, "and you can have a beer and watch the sunset."

Toni lit a cigarette and stumped off to catch up with the owners of the resort. We dropped our bags at a table and grabbed some snorkelling gear out of a big tub.

"I don't have my bikini top, remember?" whispered Fiona.

"Wear your T-shirt," I said, "it's saturated anyway."

We entered the water and swam around for a while studying the fish.

"It's not the same as Hawaii," said Fiona. "There are some different fish. And I haven't seen any turtles."

"The colours are extraordinary. I wish I had a good quality underwater camera," said Bronwyn, "they're so expensive."

The late afternoon sun dried us off as we sat on the beach. Bronwyn took some photos of us.

Fiona lay back on her elbows, her red hair dangling on to the sand behind her head. "It's beautiful here. It's paradise. And we've got it all to ourselves."

"Are you dry enough to go to the bar?" I asked, "I'm thirsty."

"All right, I was so relaxed."

A square yellow umbrella advertising *Benson and Hedges* shielded white plastic tables and chairs from the sun, and a small potted coconut palm formed a backdrop as we took our seats on the deck.

"I'll buy you that beer," said Bronwyn, and departed for the bar.

She returned with three Victoria Bitters.

"Sorry guys, the bar only serves Australian beer. At least it's cold."

"What's wrong with Australian beer?" I asked.

"It's not New Zealand beer!" Fiona and Bronwyn gave identical answers, grinned at each other and high-fived.

Australian beer went down nicely as we sat and watched the sun setting into the Pacific Ocean, while Bronwyn used up another film.

After a long dark drive at the minibuses' maximum speed, we arrived back at Toni's.

≈ ≈ ≈

My tummy emitted an embarrassing gurgling sound as we stepped off the bus. "I'm starving, all I've had to eat today is bananas and pineapples."

"There's the last of that left-over Chinese," said Fiona, "let's heat it up."

"Mmm okay, let's take it out of the containers this time so we don't have another explosion."

A young man with brown dreadlocks, and a small ring through the side of his nose, was washing a cup in the kitchen. We pulled our food out of the fridge and he introduced himself.

"Hi, I'm Nils, how are you guys?"

"I'm Simon, and this is my girlfriend Fiona. Have you just arrived in Tonga?"

"I've been here for a few weeks, in another group of islands called Ha'apai, at The Bounty Resort. My friend Kapo Folau owns it, I helped him set it up."

"Wow, we're staying there in a couple of weeks."

"You'll love it," said Nils, "there's an English guy called Sebastian staying there with Kapo; it's his home when he's between jobs. It's pretty basic, you realise that, right? Have you brought your own tent?"

"Yes, all our camping gear. We're going to be there about a week, I think."

"Fantastic, it's such a special place. You can buy all the provisions you need in Pangai; you might have to ask Kapo to give you a ride back once or twice during your stay to top up, there's no fridge or anything so fresh food doesn't keep. Oh, do you own a mosquito net? You'll need one, they're vicious bastards in Ha'apai and none of the accommodation supplies nets like Toni does. You can buy them from the little hardware store in Nuku'alofa."

"Thanks for the warning. Where are you from originally, Nils?"

"I'm from Auckland, I'm flying home tomorrow."

"Okay, Fiona's from New Zealand too, from the West Coast of the South Island." Fiona waved and smiled as she watched our food rotate in the microwave as intently as if it was the most exciting scene of her favourite television program.

"Forgive the question," I said, "but 'Nils' doesn't sound Kiwi?"

Nils laughed. "I was born in New Zealand, but my mother was from Munich and she wanted to give me a German name. I speak fluent German as well; she made sure I was bilingual from the start."

"A couple of people are staying here from Hamburg," I said.

"I already met them," said Nils, "two blond girls, right? I was talking to one of them earlier, she's a real stunner." He lowered his voice. "I think she likes me. We're going out for a bite to eat together tonight."

"Which one was it? Was her name Anja?"

"No, the other one, Claudia. She's a really friendly, chatty girl. In German, anyway. It's weird, she's travelling with that Anja, but I don't think they're friends."

"Mmm, I think you're right," I said. "They've been sightseeing around America for a few months together, but Claudia told me Anja always makes all the decisions for them both, and bosses her around because her English isn't very good. I'm pleased you're taking Claudia out. She'll be over the moon to spend time with someone else who speaks her language. When I first met her, she didn't say a word."

"Well, I better dress for my hot date. Nice to meet you, and enjoy The Bounty Resort."

He left, and we sat down to eat the Chinese. Despite its desiccation we didn't want to waste it.

≈ ≈ ≈

"What are we going to do today?" asked Fiona, the following morning, as she finished the Sanitarium.

"We need some more food. How about we go to the market?"

"All right. And you need a haircut."

"I do?"

"Yes, I don't want to be dating a hippy. Let's see if we can find a barber's."

The unmistakable smell of hot tarmac assaulted us as soon as we stepped outside. Four Tongan men in shirts and trousers were sweeping the asphalt on to the road with long-handled brooms.

"Look at them," I said. "In England, large machinery would do that job, driven by hard-hatted, orange-vested men accompanied by thousands of traffic cones in a six-mile contraflow."

"I've no idea how they work in this heat," said Fiona. "I would die."

Haphazardly parked rusty cars, vans, and pickup trucks jammed both sides of Nuku'alofa's main streets. Drawings of muscly young men carrying rugby balls decorated enormous billboards encouraging young Tongans to 'Be Healthy, Play Sport'. Tongan men sat on the edges of the broken footpaths in small groups, their feet in the streets. A car numberplate with a Jamaican reggae design and a picture of palm trees caught my eye. It had the slogan 'Sound of Polynesian Band—One Love Mei Maui'. The humid earthy smell of the tropics weaved through everything.

The open-sided market building had been designed by an architect clearly famous for municipal car parks. Fluorescent strip lights illuminated tables piled with pineapples, mangos, papaya, and bananas, alongside carrots, peppers, tomatoes, and other unidentifiable vegetables. Middle-aged ladies wearing T-shirts down to their knees chattered among the produce.

It was hard to tell which Tongan ran which stall.

Fiona picked up a long dark brown root vegetable, as tall as her. "What do you do with this?" she asked the stallholder.

"Yam. You boil. Like potato."

"Fiona, we'll hardly be able to carry that, let alone eat it all."

Fiona put the yam down.

"What about these? I've seen these before." She picked up some vegetables resembling leeks.

"Taro," said the vendor. "You cook like potato as well. Take care, poison if not cooked."

Fiona put the taro down.

"I'm all for being adventurous, but I think we should stick to what we know while we're here, we don't want to be sick."

She picked up a small green pepper from the top of a pile.

"How much is this?"

"One pa'anga."

"How much is one pa'anga again, Simon?"

"It's about 50p."

"That's a lot for a small pepper."

"One pa'anga is for all of them," said the stallholder.

"We don't need ten peppers. Can you sell us just one?"

"No. We only sell ten here."

"50p for ten peppers is a bargain, Fiona," I said, "some other people at Toni's will want them if we don't."

We put the ten peppers in a bag and added several tomatoes and onions to them. I paid the stallholder.

"Do you know where I can find a barber?" I made the time-honoured motion of scissors against my scalp.

The stallholder pointed. "Next door."

"I'll carry on shopping while you have a haircut." Fiona began picking up pineapples at another stall.

Outside the market, multi-coloured minibuses played loud rock music as their passengers entered and exited. A tiny windowless tin shed had the handwritten sign *Kosiolu* (hairdresser) above the door. I put my head in.

"Erm, hello, are you a barber?" I made the snipping motion again.

The barber indicated I should sit down on a low stool missing most of its stuffing, and he wrapped me in a black cloak. There was no mirror; I had no idea what he was about to do with my hair. As there was also no electricity for clippers, he laid out three pairs of scissors in the sizes of small, medium and terrifying.

The barber's meticulous deliberate movements cut each hair individually.

The heat in the tin shed cooked me evenly like a Christmas turkey.

My head nodded forward, and he woke me gently pulling it back.

45 minutes later he pulled the cloak off and invited me to stand. He produced a small pocket mirror and held it up to my face. Despite the basic tools and broken chair, he'd given me a hairstyle that could have earned me a job as an extra in *Grease.*

"Thank you, how much please?"

He held up two fingers. "Two pa'anga."

One pound for a haircut. At that price, I was going to have another one before we flew out.

Fiona was waiting outside the barbers with three carrier bags full of fruit and vegetables.

"Wow, hello John Travolta," she said. "He took ages."

"Look at you with your week's shopping. Anything else you need?"

"Remember Nils said we should buy a mosquito net? We'll go to the hardware store on the way back to Toni's."

Drained by the heat, we carried our shopping slowly.

"Let's buy an ice cream," said Fiona, red in the face and sweating. "We can go to Elsie's sweet store; I remember she sells them."

A young girl of about nine years old was serving at Elsie's.
"Two ice creams, please."
"Vanilla or chambo?" the girl asked.
Chambo?
What the hell is chambo?

21.
Diving with Jesus

I decided chambo must be a new exciting tropical flavour I hadn't tasted before, so I ordered one. Fiona asked for a vanilla.

The girl went to fetch the ice creams, and we sat down at a plastic table.

"It's so good to be out of the heat, isn't it Simon?"

"Mad dogs and Englishman and all that…"

The nine-year-old waitress brought Fiona's ice cream first, a standard cone with a lump of vanilla in it.

Mine arrived. The young child was carrying it with two hands. Teetering in the cone was a tower of vanilla, strawberry, and chocolate, over a foot high. It threatened to collapse under its own weight. I would have to eat it immediately before it dripped everywhere.

"One chambo," said the girl, handing it to me.

"I think," said Fiona, "*chambo* is how she pronounces 'jumbo'."

Chambo.

Jumbo.

A Tongan-sized ice cream.

After eating half the chambo I had to concede defeat and put the rest in a bin. I didn't want to waste it, but there was no way I could finish an entire tub of ice cream.

≈ ≈ ≈

Nils stood in Toni's communal living area with a backpack.

"Hey guys," he said, "how are you getting on?"

"Good thanks, Nils," I said, "are you leaving?"

"I am, and guess who's coming with me?" He smiled, a huge grin, and tossed his dreadlocks over his shoulder.

"Not Claudia?"

"Yep, we had a great evening, it was like we'd known each other for ever. This morning we went to Air New Zealand's office;

she was able to bring her flight forward and we're going on to Auckland together."

"Wow," I said, "this is sudden."

"I know," said Nils, "but it feels so right."

At that moment Claudia entered with her own bags. She greeted Nils in German, kissed him, and said 'Hello' to us.

Kesi's voice called from outside, "the minibus is going to the airport now."

Nils picked up both his and Claudia's bags. As they were leaving, Anja marched in, red faced, and screamed at them in rapid-fire aggressive German. We didn't understand the words, but she clearly wasn't wishing them a pleasant trip. She stormed off, sobbing.

Nils hid his face behind his hair and studied the floor.

Claudia looked straight ahead towards the front door.

She took her cabin baggage in one hand and linked her other arm through Nils's.

She smiled. For the first time since I had met her, she was making her own decisions.

"Good luck, guys," said Fiona. "I'm glad you two met each other."

"Give my regards to Kapo," called Nils as they left.

"That was a bit dramatic," I said to Fiona, when we were alone.

"I could see that coming. Claudia took the first opportunity to split. That Anja girl has some serious personality problems."

We didn't see Anja again. Toni told us later she had left the next day.

≈ ≈ ≈

The dive boat puttered gently away from the wharf, Jan at the wheel staring dead ahead, his mouth in a straight line. I had set myself a private challenge to make him laugh today, but his mood was as serious as an undertaker in an epidemic.

"This place drives me mad," he said. "I give a Tongan man a job as my gardener, and he steals my coconuts."

"Maybe he really needs them?" I said, "I think some people here have hardly any food."

"The problem is," said Jan, "the Tongans don't have a concept of ownership. Historically, all possessions are communal. An excellent theory, in that everyone gets looked after by their families and nobody goes without essentials, not so great if people help themselves to stuff you consider to be yours."

"It must have been hard adjusting to life here as a European."

"I'm not a rich man. I have my boat, and my car, and little else. I don't even own the house we live in. But my wife's family believe I'm an incredibly wealthy *palangi*, and I should support all of them. I mean, I'm happy to help with money they need for essential medical care. But the other day, my mother-in-law wanted me to pay to have her legs waxed. She's never had them waxed before in her life; it was something she'd seen in a magazine. Because I'm a 'rich westerner', she thinks I can give her unlimited funds for that sort of thing."

I understood why Jan's mood was morose.

I needed to change the subject.

"Jan, where are we diving today?"

He brightened.

"Today, Simon, we're going to do four dives. I'll give you free diving today, because I've seen you're competent, and I need a bit of help."

Wow, free diving.

"Of course, Jan. What do you need me to do?"

"Yesterday, I had a phone call from Fafa Island Resort, a short distance off the coast here. They want us to collect two of their guests who are going to dive with us. I think they're not experienced, so we'll all dive together. I'll lead the dives, and you can follow at the rear to make sure nobody gets left behind. Afterwards we'll drop them back and have some lunch. I brought some fruit to eat. This afternoon we've a similar job. I'll tell you about it later."

I loved that he referred to it as a job. I was going to be working as a dive professional on a tropical island.

"It's about three kilometres to Fafa Island. While I'm steering, could you please assemble our guests' dive gear? I think you know how to do that."

I gathered the various components we'd need.

Jan increased speed as we left the wharf, while I balanced on the rear deck, shifting from one bare foot to the other with the motion of the boat, gazing at the tropical sea, sun on my back, assembling tanks and buoyancy devices. If a competition for 'most content marine employee' existed, I would be on the podium.

After a few minutes, the tone of the engine changed. We couldn't be there already. What was wrong? I looked forward through the wheelhouse. An open boat was approaching us, with three people in it. The man standing at the wheel was waving at us with his entire arm.

"What's up with them, Jan? Do they need help?"

"It's the boat from Fafa Island. Let's see what they want."

We motored slowly over to them until we were alongside.

Jan greeted the driver. "Hi Alan, everything okay?"

It's so cool how all the people working in the tourist industry here know each other.

"Hi, Jan. I've brought your customers to you. I was heading into town, so I thought we'd meet halfway."

Two men sat in the boat's bow. One had a closely cropped beard, and they both had Mediterranean sunburnt skin. Jan invited them to step over into our boat. I helped them board.

"Hi guys, I'm Jan, your instructor, and this is Simon, who's working with me today."

I felt proud to be introduced as his assistant.

I can't let them know this is my first day on the job.

The man with the beard spoke.

"Hello. I'm Pedro. This is my brother, Hesoos."

"Which country are you from?" I asked.

"From Spain. We're travelling round the world and we're here a few days. It's beautiful here, no people. Not like Spain."

I agreed it wasn't like Spain.

Jan pulled out a clipboard and gave it to me.

"Simon, please ask our guests to fill out their details on this dive log. Name, address, and the rest. I'll start driving."

I gave the clipboard to Pedro. He filled in his details and passed the form to his brother.

Hesoos wrote, and returned the completed document to me.

I scanned it.

His name wasn't Hesoos.

It was Jesus.

Pronounced 'Hesoos'.

My first ever day working in the industry, and I was going to be diving with Jesus.

Our first dive site was a sunken freighter off Makaha island, close to where Jan had shown me the organ coral. Jan anchored, and we all donned our dive gear. Jesus helped Pedro, instructing him in rapid Spanish where he should put his arms.

Jan addressed the brothers. "I'll enter the water first, and you both please follow me. Stay close to me and to each other. Simon will swim behind. If you have any problem, Simon or I will help you."

Who'll help me if I have a problem?

I dismissed this thought, as I was now a highly experienced dive professional.

Jan jumped into the water, and Pedro, Jesus and I followed. They both seemed to know the basics, which was a relief. I didn't want to be putting my rescue diver training into practice if I could help it.

Jan pointed into the water. "If you look down, you can see the wreck. It's shallow here; we can stay underwater a long time. Everybody ready? Let's go."

Jan gave the 'thumbs down' signal, indicating we should descend.

We submerged, and Pedro plummeted to the sea floor.

Oh great, day one at work and I've killed my first customer.

Pedro sat on the ocean floor surrounded by a cloud of sand, his hands flailing around as he tried to steady himself and operate his equipment. I helped him inflate his buoyancy device, and he floated just above the bottom. I gripped his tank valve to keep him near to me and prevent a reoccurrence. Once Jan and Jesus had appeared, Jan gave the *okay* sign, I responded, and we followed them as they swam.

All was silent in the underwater world. Pedro drifted beside me, more relaxed.

The wreck loomed ahead of us, a foreign invader in these pristine waters. She lay on her side, murky brown and green, shoals of fish surrounding her. Large fish swam past, with smaller accomplices hitching a ride in their slipstream. A stingray hovered underneath us, and settled, burying itself in the sand.

Jan pointed at the entrance to the wreck and wagged his finger left and right. The implication was clear: 'do not enter'. We circled the wreck, our slow approach making fish hide in the portholes. We looked in, and they scattered.

Pedro showed me his air gauge. One third remaining. It was time to return to the boat. I gave Jan the 'thumbs-up' sign, meaning *time to swim to the surface.* We swam diagonally upwards, following Jan. I helped Pedro slow his ascent. I didn't want him to get the bends, a serious condition divers suffer from, caused by ascending too fast. I knew the nearest working decompression chamber was in Fiji. The one in Tonga was broken, like much of the infrastructure here.

We surfaced a few metres from the boat and took our air regulators out of our mouths.

"How was that?" Jan asked the Spaniards.

"Amazing, I've never seen anything like it." Pedro spoke some rapid Spanish with Jesus, who nodded.

We boarded the boat and Jan started the engine. I heard the anchor chain clanking up.

"Now we'll go to Pangimotu Island. Simon, could you please change all the tanks?"

Changing four people's tanks was hard work. I didn't care, I pretended I was an expert marine employee who'd been working on dive boats all my life.

We dropped anchor near Pangimotu island. Nuku'alofa shimmered in the haze off the starboard side.

"Here we're going to dive a wreck that sank in the 1982 hurricane," said Jan.

Tonga specialised in sunken boats.

Pedro managed better on this dive, and it was more relaxing for me.

We returned the Spaniards to Fafa Island and anchored a short distance offshore.

Sparkling turquoise sea extended to the horizon, as three flying fish ploooped nearby.

"What's the plan for this afternoon, skipper?" I asked.

"First, we'll have some lunch. Then I've a real treat for you."

Jan produced a container full of tropical fruit, which we ate while he talked.

"We're going to collect our next customers from Royal Sunset Island Resort, on Atata Island, a long way further out to sea. They're an American couple. I dived with them yesterday; they know what they're doing. You won't need me to lead the dives. I'll stay on the boat, and you can be in charge."

In charge.

Me.

Leading the dives.

I tried not to show how anxious I was about this.

"They want to swim with sharks, so we'll take them to Hakaumama'o reef reserve. It's twenty kilometres out to sea, the furthest reef away from Nuku'alofa. There are small reef sharks there."

Great. My first ever experience leading dives for paying customers and I'm being thrown to the sharks.

"Jan, is there a knack to leading these dives? I mean, I haven't dived this spot before, how will I know where to go? And how do you find the boat again so easily?"

"Great questions. Here's the trick. The reef has several coral heads. I'll tell you which direction to swim in once we anchor. Count the coral heads, and once you've used about one third of your air, turn round and come back again. Count the coral heads on the way back as you pass them, and you'll be right under the boat."

"Sounds good. What about the second dive?"

"That's even easier. It's on the other side of the reef, a two-minute boat ride from the first one. We'll anchor in my usual spot; you drop down and follow the edge of the reef. Once you've about two-thirds of your air left, you turn round and follow the reef back again. You'll be fine."

I was proud Jan had trusted me to give his clients an enjoyable experience, and I didn't want to disappoint him.

"Finished?" Jan packed the fruit away. "Can you please change the tanks while we drive to Atata Island?"

At Royal Sunset Resort's wharf, the Americans introduced themselves as Rick and Pamela. Rick carried a large underwater camera. He passed it to me as he stepped awkwardly over the edge of the boat, his tummy moulding itself to the rail. His steel grey hair swept up in a quiff, and his polo shirt displayed the logo *Canyon Golf Club.*

I reckoned Pamela wasn't much older than me. She wore huge Prada sunglasses and had spent some time perfecting her bleached blonde hair and make-up, as if she were about to star in *Dynasty*. I found this odd as she was going underwater. They accepted Jan's explanation I would lead the dives today without question.

Wealthy, paying divers relying on me for a great holiday experience.

I hope my nerves don't show. I hope I don't make any mistakes.

To give the impression that I knew what I was doing, I untied the ropes and coiled them neatly, while Jan pulled away from the dock.

We sped up, heading for the open sea, and I struck a pose as if I worked on a dive boat every day of my life. The American couple talked to each other and not to me. I realised there was an unseen barrier between the paying customers and the staff.

Nuku'alofa was distant on one horizon, and out to sea nothing was visible but water. We anchored at the outer reef. I looked over the side and could see the first coral head.

Rick helped Pamela with her gear, and they refused my offer of assistance. I was becoming more nervous.

What if something happens?

I had visions of a Stetson-clad Texan prosecutor pacing up and down in a Houston court, asking me where I was at the time in question.

Jan called me in to the wheelhouse. "It's important when you're leading a dive to enter the water before your customers. Then if one of them has a problem, you're in the water and you can help. I think they're ready, you'd better kit up."

I rushed to put my familiar gear on, and with my hand holding my mask to my face, I tumbled backwards over the side. Rick and Pamela followed me, and we gathered at the surface.

"Everybody ready?" I asked.

Jan called from the boat. "Just a minute, Simon." He beckoned me over. "I think you might need this."

He handed me my weight belt and laughed. "You won't sink very far down without it."

Embarrassed, I took the weight belt and put it on. As I swam back to the other two divers, he chuckled behind me. I had achieved my goal of making him laugh, not in quite the way I had intended.

Thank goodness Rick and Pamela hadn't seen.

My 'thumbs down' signal invited them to descend close to the first coral head.

I led the way.

One coral head. Two coral heads.

Little white-tipped reef sharks swam around us, and Rick took several pictures.

Three coral heads.

A colossal fish, bigger than the sharks, swam into view. Rick photographed Pamela with the giant fish in the background and turned to me, making the *okay* sign. Even though his air regulator hid his mouth, I could see from his eyes he was smiling. I relaxed.

Dive leading's easy, I'm enjoying this.

We reached the fourth coral head.

I checked my air. Two-thirds left. Time to return.

Rick had his camera close to the coral head and his flash reflected from underneath it. Fish would be hiding there, and I guessed he'd discovered something good to photograph. I turned round to find Pamela.

Something was wrong.

Her air regulator wasn't in her mouth. She had no air.

Oh shit.

22.
A Meal of Vomit

I swam over to Pamela as fast as I could. She was scooping her right arm behind her, trying to find the hose that connected her air regulator to her tank, and her eyes were wide and panicked.

Help! *What do I do*?

Her air regulator dangled just out of her reach. I grabbed it and shoved it into her mouth, pushing with my flat hand against it. My rescue diver training had taught me alarmed divers sometimes spit their regulator out in their terror. I made a slow hand movement repeatedly up to my mouth and then away again, meaning *breathe slowly*. She calmed down as she discovered she had air again. A few seconds later, her eyes returned to normal, and she began to look at me, not through me. I made the closed thumb and forefinger signal; *are you okay*? She showed the same sign back to me; *I'm okay*.

We swam together towards Rick. He was still snapping pictures, unaware of what had happened. I made a sign to him to indicate we were returning to the boat.

I kept close to Pamela.

Four coral heads, three, two, one, and the bottom of the boat appeared above us. I gave the 'thumbs-up' sign, and we ascended, surfacing a few metres away from the ladder.

"That was grand," said Rick. "The giant wrasse, the sharks. I think I took some great photos. You should have seen that lobster under the coral head."

"Rick, I nearly goddamned drowned," said Pamela, sounding most unlike a Dynasty actress. "If it wasn't for Simon, I'd be dead."

"What the hell happened?" Rick turned to me as if I were responsible.

"It's not Simon's fault," said Pamela. "You always tell me to take my regulator out so you can see my smile in the photos. I'm not doing that ever again. I dropped my regulator; couldn't find it again, and you went off like a jerk with your stupid camera, and left me."

Her expression changed from anger to a smile. "Thank you so much Simon. I'm so glad you knew what to do."

Rick looked annoyed. He wasn't used to being addressed in this fashion in front of the hired hand.

"Where's the next dive?" he asked, changing the subject.

"On the other side of the reef, a two-minute boat ride," I said, as if I had been there several times this week already.

We climbed back on board, and the expert deckhand, dive leader and now lifesaver changed the tanks again for his adoring clientele.

I remembered Jan's advice about the second dive and led Rick and Pamela along the reef. The sound like crinkling cellophane reminded me to search for the parrot fish, who made this noise as they tore weed off the rocks.

Rick took multiple pictures of the various coral formations. His flash lit up in my peripheral vision, while I kept a careful eye on Pamela.

We finished the dive and returned the Americans to Atata island.

"Simon, you've just been tremendous," said Pamela, as I helped her off the boat.

She held my hand a little too long, making sure Rick was noticing. She mounted her sunglasses on her nose, and strode off up the jetty, without waiting for her husband.

Rick took his wallet out of his pocket. He looked down at the floor, and then up at me. "Thank you for what you did back there. And thanks for leading the dives. Here, something for you."

He placed a note in my hand and followed Pamela into the resort.

I opened my palm.

"Jan, he gave me fifty pa'anga."

"The Americans tip well, don't they? You've earned it, dive leader."

Fifty pa'anga was only twenty-five pounds, but I felt prouder of today's salary than any wages I had earned in an office.

We motored back to Nuku'alofa, while I explained to Jan what happened on the first dive.

"Wow, you really earned your tip," he said, "I bet you never thought you'd put your rescue diver training into practice today."

After unloading the boat Jan dropped me back at Toni's.

"Fiona," I said, "you'll never guess what I've done today? I've been on four dives, I led two of them, I saved a lady's life, and a rich American tipped me."

"That's exciting. What happened?"

I explained how I rescued Pamela, embellishing the story significantly for Fiona's benefit.

"You're amazing. How much did he give you?"

"Fifty pa'anga. Twenty-five pounds. Anyway, how was your day?" I asked her.

"Well, nothing as exciting as yours. I popped out to the supermarket to buy some groceries and spent most of the afternoon reading my book in the living area. I met some new people too, Lisa and Nicole, they're student doctors from Australia who've come to work at the hospital here for a few weeks. They're having a drink at the International Pacific Hotel this evening, and they've invited us to join them."

"Sounds great. I'll have to wear my Hawaiian shirt again."

A cold shower and a shirt later and the hero marine rescuer was ready to dazzle two more ladies with his stories of saving helpless divers from certain death.

The International Pacific Hotel was owned by the Tongan government. The intention of this enterprise was to provide business-standard accommodation which would attract the high-spending better type of foreign tourist, instead of young backpackers content to rough it at places like Toni's.

In this aim it failed completely. The International Pacific Hotel was an excellent demonstration of why governments shouldn't run tourist establishments.

The bar overlooked the swimming pool. A border of weathered, cracked tiles surrounded a rectangle of opaque green water. A small family of ducks crapped on a single broken lounger. Large, unkempt bushes dangled into the quagmire. I couldn't imagine a pool well-heeled guests would be less likely to swim in.

Fiona introduced me to the young Australian doctors. Lisa's dark-brown ponytail framed her Mediterranean features. Nicole wore sunglasses partly covering her freckled face.

"G'day, Simon," said Lisa, raising her glass of beer, "How ya going?"

"I'm well, thanks." I pulled out my American lifesaving earnings. "What would you like to drink, Fiona?"

Nicole spoke up. "It doesn't matter what Fiona wants to drink, all they serve is beer, and it's not exactly cold either."

I turned to the bartender. "Two beers please."

Lisa and Nicole were in Tonga on a scheme where Australian trainee doctors work as interns in Tongan hospitals. It was a mutually beneficial arrangement; the students received real-world medical experience and in return, Tonga obtained desperately needed skills.

The bartender produced the warm beers, and I entertained Fiona and the doctors with stories about my diving adventures, being sure to describe Pamela as being on death's door when I found her, lifeless and non-responsive, about to be consumed by a passing killer whale.

"They were staying at a resort on an island?" asked Lisa. "Do those offshore resorts seem nice? This one's a dump."

"I didn't see Fafa Island, but Royal Sunset Resort on Atata Island looked stunning from the dock. There's a beautiful beach right outside, with loungers and umbrellas."

"Atata island takes day trippers," said Fiona. "There's a sign at the wharf. I think the boat leaves at 10 a.m. Shall we go down one morning?"

"Great idea," said Nicole, "we've both got a free day tomorrow, before we start work at the hospital. Would tomorrow be okay with you?"

"Sounds like a plan."

We sculled the warm beers and walked back to Toni's.

I hugged Fiona as we strolled. "You mentioned you'd been to the supermarket. What's for dinner tonight?"

"How do you fancy nachos?"

"Oh yes please, I do enjoy this traditional Tongan cooking."

"You are funny, Simon."

≈ ≈ ≈

The next day, at the dock, a sign next to a small catamaran advertised *Atata Island Royal Sunset Resort.* We joined the short queue for tickets, behind a family with an annoying-looking small boy. Lisa, Nicole and Fiona had packed their swimmers and books and were all ready for a day's sunbathing. I was looking forward to snorkelling; I knew what treasures the waters around the island held. I wondered if Rick and Pamela were still staying, or even still speaking to each other.

The crew cast off the ropes, and the catamaran motored out of the harbour. Fiona stood at the rail, looking over the side, her dark red hair streaming behind her in the wind. I was dating an actress in a poster for a dramatic nautical period drama.

As soon as we left the shelter of the breakwater, the catamaran sped up, and we bounced across waves whipped up by the breeze. I gripped the rail next to Fiona, rising and falling with the motion of the boat. Small islands lay ahead of us on the horizon, and I tried to pick out Atata. Seabirds flew above, crying to each other. The smell of the salt filled my nostrils as the occasional cool spray splashed my face. I had never felt more alive.

"Simon?"

"Yes, babe?"

"I'm going to be sick."

Fiona's skin colour had turned even whiter than usual.

"Keep watching the horizon," I said. "Stare at the islands ahead of us. Don't look down at the boat or the sea."

Fiona ignored my advice and slumped on the deck, her head in her hands.

Lisa and Nicole looked concerned.

"Seasickness," I said, "she'll be all right once we stop."

"I reckon we're almost halfway," said Lisa. "Hold on, Fiona, not much longer."

Fiona looked up at me. I had seen darker photocopying paper.

"If you're going to throw up," I said, "move over to the other side of the boat. You don't want to be sick into the wind."

Fiona crawled across the moving deck and lay with her head near the side. She closed her eyes.

I looked toward Atata island. A small boat departed from the Royal Sunset Resort dock and headed in our direction.

Lisa rubbed Fiona's back. "Nearly there. Stay with us."

Fiona opened her eyes briefly. "I just want to die."

Even though this was only seasickness, I was grateful we had two doctors on board.

The little boat said *Royal Sunset Resort* on the side. The catamaran slowed down to meet it, and our crew prepared their ropes and fenders.

As the two boats touched together on one side of the catamaran, on the other side Fiona vomited generously into the sea. She lay down, recovering.

The small boy looked over at where Fiona had thrown up, his eyes wide. A malevolent grin appeared on his face.

"Mum, Mum, look at the fish! The fish are eating the lady's sick."

Despite the image he described, none of us could help ourselves. We all looked into the sea. Hundreds of tropical fish painted in multiple primary colours feasted on Fiona's regurgitated breakfast. The scene was at once beautiful and gruesome.

Fiona looked up at me and smiled. "I feel better now."

We all clambered over on to the smaller boat which took us to Atata Island.

A wooden jetty led from the dock, and a sign that might have once been part of a shipwreck welcomed us to the Royal Sunset Resort. Workers swept the beach with long metal rakes, steering around architectural plants. A man whose shirt logo advertised him as an employee greeted us in the deserted central open bar area.

"Where are all the guests?" I asked him.

"There aren't any at all today. We had a couple, but they left this morning. You've got the resort to yourselves. You can use all the facilities; this afternoon we can take you snorkelling to a reef near here, and we include a barbecue lunch in your ticket."

"Great," said Fiona, "I'm hungry."

"I'm not surprised," I said, "you, err, haven't had breakfast. Well, you did, but then…"

"Thank you, Simon, you don't need to remind me."

Fiona walked off with Lisa and Nicole to some loungers on the beach. They soon lay in their bikinis, reading magazines and chatting about stuff that would interest no-one with a Y chromosome.

I pulled on my snorkelling gear and entered the sea. The beach sloped off quickly, and the fish were sparse here as there wasn't any coral. I didn't want to swim out too far as I wasn't familiar with the currents. I had no desire to become a newspaper headline: *English snorkeller missing in Tonga, last seen heading for Fiji. Presumed eaten by man-eating sharks.*

Sea grass covered the sandy bottom in an underwater field. I was drifting slowly when I saw it. A huge turtle, a few metres below me. Its mouth grabbed clumps of grass and tore them off. The action was identical to that a horse would make in a paddock. I hovered over it and watched, following closely behind, as it progressed on its journey. After a few minutes, it swam up to the surface diagonally, took a small breath and dived again. I wanted Fiona to watch the turtle with me, and I looked up to shout, to tell her to grab her snorkel. I was alarmed to find the shore was a very long way in the distance.

23. Sore Bottoms and Ambassadors

I could see the three girls lounging on the beach, but they might as well have been on the moon; there was no way they could hear me shout. I swam, strong strokes, face down, breathing through my snorkel. The turtle was forgotten.

Ten minutes extreme front crawl returned me to the shallow water, relieved I was no longer in danger. This was a lesson to me.

"Fiona, guess what happened. I swam a bit too far out, it was scary, you looked miles away."

"Oh, wow. I didn't know you were in the water."

That was a close brush with disaster. Nobody knew where I was. If I'd drifted out any further, I'd never have been found.

A deep gong announced lunch. Plastic tables and chairs under yellow and brown umbrellas formed the dining room. I bought beers from the bar; we helped ourselves to meat and salad, and sat down with the doctors.

"How are you feeling?" I asked Fiona, "are you going to manage any food?"

"I'm fine," she said, picking up a crispy chicken drumstick, "it was just the motion of the boat."

"Pleased to hear you've recovered. The meal's good here, isn't it?"

"It's amazing how filling meat and salad is. And beer. I hope I'm okay on the journey back."

"Oh, I don't know, I think the fish appreciated your donation."

Fiona playfully prodded me.

We ate far too much, and lay down again flat on our backs spread out like blubbery starfish.

A voice called from the dock, "the snorkelling trip is leaving now."

"Anyone coming?" I asked, forgetting my earlier brush with death.

"I don't want to go on any more boats than necessary today," said Fiona, "I'll stay here."

"Me too," said Lisa, "I'll keep you company. I've eaten so much I'd sink."

"I'll come with you, Simon," said Nicole. "I've never been snorkelling."

I entered dive leader mode again. "You haven't? You're in for a treat."

Nicole borrowed some snorkelling gear, and we boarded the little boat. It motored a short distance from the dock and dropped anchor near a large coral head. I educated her in the gentle art of breathing underwater without drowning, and we jumped off the side. We swam towards the coral head, looking at the colourful fish.

"This is amazing," said Nicole, as she floated on her back for a rest, "is snorkelling always this good?"

That was a hard question to answer. I'd seen all these fish before, but I didn't want to downplay her adventure.

"The first time you do it's magical. Then after that, sometimes it's good, sometimes you're not experiencing anything new. And then there's the odd occasion it blows your mind and exceeds all the others."

"Sounds like my love life," said Nicole, and we both had a good laugh at that.

The small boat returned us to the dock. Lisa and Fiona were both fast asleep in the sun. Lisa's Italian heritage allowed her to do this without any noticeable effect, but Fiona's skin was turning the colour of a good quality piece of smoked salmon from Selfridge's food hall.

"Fiona, wake up."

"What? Far out, Simon, I was sleeping off the beer."

"I, um, think you should get in the shade. Have you got sunscreen on?"

Fiona looked down at her pink tummy.

"Oops. I'll get dressed."

She threw on her T-shirt, and slopped sunblock on her legs.

The wind had dropped on the return journey, and Fiona denied the fish a meal of vomit.

"What are you guys doing for dinner?" asked Lisa, as we walked back to Toni's. "Kesi recommended a Chinese restaurant near here. Would you like to come with us?"

"We've been to that one already. We could probably order the large sized meal between four of us and have enough left over to feed more people than the Salvation Army. Do you fancy Chinese tonight, Fiona?"

"Why not? We can bring the leftovers back for tomorrow again. Ow, don't touch me. Mind my sunburn."

≈ ≈ ≈

A hot wind blew across our faces, and the wet earth steamed under a blanket of grey cloud, as we stood outside the guest house early the following day. Toni had hired us two bicycles, manufactured only slightly more recently than penny-farthings, and Fiona leant hers up, as she studied the basic map in the guidebook.

"Where do you want to go first?" I asked her.

"How about going back to the blowholes? With this wind they should be even more spectacular than last time."

I recalled our experiences with Bronwyn.

"Sounds good," I said. "Let's try to take a photo without getting soaked. I've brought the tripod."

We mounted the boneshakers, and set off across the island. People waved from passing cars and vans. The further we rode from Nuku'alofa, the lighter the traffic became. We dodged round puddles as tarmac gave way to potholed gravel roads, the thick grass on both sides punctuated by noisily rustling palm trees. We pushed hard, the hot wind competing with our efforts.

Fiona stopped. "My bum hurts. And my sunburn's rubbing."

"These saddles aren't the most comfortable, are they? Let's have a break."

We lay the bikes on the ground, as we investigated our surroundings.

I realised I had only ever seen tropical fruit in a shop.

"What are these spiky plants?" I asked, "there's some kind of fruit in the middle of them."

"They're pineapples, I think."

"I thought pineapples grew on trees, like apples."

"Nope, these are definitely pineapples."

I took a picture of the pineapple plant.

"How about those trees on the other side of the road?" I asked. "Those tall sticks with fruit stuck to them?"

We walked over to the sticks.

"I think that's how papaya grows," said Fiona. "They're the same as the ones at the market."

I photographed Fiona beside a papaya plant. It was twice as tall as her.

"Do you reckon we could pick one?" I asked.

"I don't think we should. These are somebody's livelihood."

Fiona felt a papaya. "They're rock hard anyway. Not ready yet."

Her bum had recovered, and we continued.

Dramatic gigantic waves churned up by the wind crashed into the blowhole rocks, and spray shot metres high into the air. Standing up was a challenge, as we gazed down.

Fiona held on to me. "There's no way today we could reach the spot where Bronwyn had us posing," she said, "we'd be swept away. It's much rougher."

"This scenery is stunning," I said, "and there's no-one else here. Imagine if this was in Europe. There'd be a coach park, an entry fee, a café and hordes of tourists."

"Where do you want to go now?" asked Fiona. "I'm not sure I can manage an entire day riding on this saddle."

I looked at the guidebook.

"Let's head back to town via the king and queen's house. Maybe we'll catch a glimpse of them. I so want to see the queen."

"I thought they lived at the palace?"

"The guide says they've a country home outside Nuku'alofa. We may as well ride past; it's just a minor detour."

Decorative red wrought-iron gates were closed across a driveway, behind which attractive wooden buildings stood together. One had arched windows, and must have been the chapel. A small sentry box inside the gates contained a single soldier. He didn't seem to mind us being there, so I snapped a picture of the Tongan equivalent of Windsor Castle. It was all extremely low key. As there was a distinct lack of monarchs visible, we headed away and returned on the road towards Toni's.

The traffic increased as we re-entered Nuku'alofa and paused outside the guest house.

"We've hired the bikes the whole day," I said. "I know they're a bit uncomfortable, but d'you think we could ride along the sea front for a bit this afternoon? We could take a picnic, and have plenty of stops."

"I think I'm going to need a break every ten minutes the way my bottom's feeling."

We stuffed some crackers and fruit into a bag and picked the bikes up again.

It didn't seem to matter which direction we were cycling; the high wind blew against us and slowed us down. We passed the still-deserted Royal palace and headed parallel to the sea. A group of Tongan ladies and their children were swimming, fully clothed. The kids laughed and waved. We stopped and I raised my camera, entranced by the scene.

A mostly submerged Tongan lady wearing a voluminous dark brown dress addressed her offspring. "Look," she said, "that palangi is taking a photo of you."

This was the first time a Tongan had called me a *palangi.*

I didn't feel comfortable being referred to as a long pig, and wondered if the Tongans had really abandoned their ancient habit of snacking on westerners.

A Union Jack flag flew above a white wooden building, and we stopped for some further bottom-recuperation.

"British High Commission." Fiona read the sign outside. "The front door's open, d'you reckon we could go in?"

"Why not? I'm British, after all."

As we leant our bikes against the white picket fence, an elderly white Range Rover pulled up, with the numberplate, GB1.

"Simon, it's the ambassador."

We waited respectfully for his excellency to appear. I imagined him to be in a dress uniform, perhaps with a tall hat with ostrich feathers. I wondered if we were supposed to salute.

A small, fat middle-aged man with white hair and an open-necked shirt climbed out of the Range Rover. He didn't have a dress uniform or ostrich feathers. He waved at us and waddled into the building.

"I suppose Tonga isn't a particularly prestigious posting." I said.

Fiona giggled.

We read the newspapers in the reception of the High Commission, eating our snacks. The headlines announced 2000 people had died in a cyclone, fatal plane crashes had occurred in Nigeria and India, and a bomb had exploded in Moscow.

"It's so good to be away from all this, Fiona. I haven't missed reading the news at all."

"Look at this photo of Princess Diana." Fiona showed me the front of a colour supplement. "She's so beautiful. I wish I'd seen her while I was in London. She's my favourite royal. Never mind, there'll be plenty of other chances I suppose."

"I'm sure the opportunity will present itself somewhere," I said. "She gets around. It's amazing to think how many magazine covers she's been on. She'll still have the paparazzi hounding her when she's 60."

≈ ≈ ≈

We spent another three weeks in Nuku'alofa, relaxing, walking, chatting to other guests who came and went. Jan employed me regularly as a dive leader, although I didn't save any more American tourists. Bronwyn departed for New Zealand, her camera slung round her neck as if she were a Beirut war reporter. Lisa and Nicole stumbled through at all hours, the exhaustion showing as they explained that often they were the only doctors on night duty at the hospital.

Tongan life continued at a somnolent pace.

Choirs sang.

Nightclubs dooofed.

Dogs barked.

Chickens pokked.

It was Friday.

The day before our flight to the Ha'apai Islands.

Fiona prodded me. "Wake up Simon; it's our last day here. What's on the agenda?"

"Well, we must do a few jobs before we fly to Ha'apai. We must go to Royal Tongan Airlines and reconfirm we want to disembark there."

"Oh yes, I'd forgotten about that."

"And we need to cash some more travellers' cheques, and work out what we're taking with us and what we're leaving at Toni's. The luggage allowance on the Ha'apai flight is only twelve kilos each. With the tent and dive gear, we won't have much room left."

≈ ≈ ≈

At the airline office, ceiling fans rotated slowly as large flies dodged their blades. Brown chipped Formica furniture with thin metal legs stood on diarrhoea coloured carpet. We waited on a dark orange wooden-armed sofa, until summoned by a serious looking Royal Tongan Airlines lady. We were an inconvenience to her, interrupting her busy day doing absolutely nothing.

"Hello," I said, "we're flying to the Ha'apai Islands tomorrow and wanted to reconfirm the plane will drop us off, as we heard it doesn't stop there unless you ask in advance."

"No, it stops in Ha'apai every day."

"Really? Because our travel agent told us we had to ask to get off."

"I don't know why they'd tell you that. It always stops in Ha'apai."

"Okay then…."

We left, not knowing what else to say.

"This is Tonga," I said to Fiona. "I don't have much confidence it's actually going to stop."

"What can we do, Simon? The lady said it stops in Ha'apai. We can't exactly disagree with her."

"I know, I'm remembering what Ben said about reconfirming."

"Well, we've reconfirmed. Stop stressing."

We were eating dinner in the kitchen, when a new arrival entered.

"Hey guys, I'm Matt. Nice ta meet ye."

His shaved head and round glasses didn't match his Scottish accent.

"Did you arrive here today?" I asked.

"Aye, just flew in from Ha'apai. I've been there for the last two weeks."

"We're headed there tomorrow. What's it like?"

"I don't know why you're bothering, there's nothing there. You have to make your own entertainment, there's nothing to do at all. It's just beaches with no facilities. Nae restaurants, nightclubs, or anything. I was so bored. I'm away oot of here tomorrow. Enjoy yerselves."

He walked out.

I couldn't wait to fly to the Ha'apai Islands. They sounded perfect.

24.
Nun in a Small Plane

"Pok."

"Pok pok pok."

"Pok pok pok pok pok pok."

The chicken alarm clock advised me it was time to prepare for our flight.

Fiona sat on the floor, already dressed, wiping her face with a flannel.

I pulled some clothes on, and studied the backpacks.

"I wish Toni had a weighing scale," I said, "these bags must be heavier than twelve kilos." I picked one up to test this theory.

"Well, take out your dive gear," said Fiona.

"Erm, no. I need my dive gear. I wonder if they weigh the hand luggage. Can you find any heavy small items?"

"I've heard they not only weigh the hand luggage, they weigh the passengers so they can balance the plane. If they'd four huge Tongan men on one side, it'd fly around in circles."

"Can we take out any more clothes? It won't be cold."

"I've only brought one jumper for the evenings. And my rain jacket which I'm planning on wearing."

Rain jacket.

Wearing.

That was the answer. In London, we'd bought two high quality rain jackets, made of light material that allowed your skin to breathe; even in humid conditions you didn't get sweaty. They had huge pockets, so deep you could lose a limb in them.

"Fiona, you're a genius."

"I am?"

"If we put on our rain jackets and fill the pockets with small heavy stuff, they can't ask us to empty them," I said. "We could put our books in, for instance."

We unpacked everything again.

"Okay," I said, "apart from books, what's small and heavy that'll fit in a jacket pocket?"

We identified a torch, a camera, and two tins of spaghetti.

"Simon, why are we taking spaghetti to Ha'apai?"

"Err, they might not sell it there?"

"You're right, they might not, but there'll be other food. Let's leave the spaghetti behind. It weighs over half a kilo."

I reluctantly added the tins to the bags that would remain at Toni's.

Kesi's voice summoned us.

"Fiona, Simon, the bus is leaving for the airport."

We stuffed the remaining loose items into our packs, and put the other bags in Toni's cupboard.

"I hope they don't charge us extra," I said, "I still reckon my bag is overweight. It's mostly dive gear."

"It feels strange. I'm sure I haven't packed enough clothes," said Fiona. "I expect we'll spend a lot of time in swimmers."

We climbed into the minibus, and Kesi trundled it back to the airport.

≈ ≈ ≈

A cleaner in a loose floral dress drew a mop lazily backwards and forwards over the terminal floor. She flicked a duster at the occasional passing fly, and steered round three airport workers sitting on the ground eating bread. A plump security guard occupied two seats. His head lolled at an angle, a peaked cap hid his face, and he snored with his entire body, the sound rising above the swish-swish of the mop.

A family of Tongans were in line before us at the check-in desk. I watched as they placed their bags on the scales and the electronic display showed the number of kilos, which wasn't visible to me. No conveyor belt was present to whisk the bags away through black plastic hanging flappy things to some unseen location. Instead, a door behind the check-in desk opened, and two airport workers collected the bags and carried them away.

"It's a manual baggage belt." whispered Fiona. "Very environmentally friendly."

The check-in lady asked the male passenger to step on the scales. She made a note, and invited his wife to do the same. Their teenagers were excused the weighing process. The family chatted and laughed with her.

"Fiona, they're not weighing the hand luggage. I'm going to put my dive regulator into it."

The dive regulator was small, but weighed around five kilos. I took it out of my backpack and stuffed it into my cabin bag.

The family in front completed their socialising. At the counter, I handed the lady our passports and reservation details. She returned the passports without looking at them.

"It's an internal flight," she said.

She looked at her screen.

"Quiet here today," I said, conversationally.

She smiled. "It's quiet here every day. It's only busy when Air New Zealand comes in. Or Royal Tongan from Auckland. Are you checking in for the Va'vau flight?"

"We are, but we're getting out in the Ha'apai Islands. The plane is stopping in Ha'apai, isn't it?"

Fiona rolled her eyes at me.

"Of course," said the check-in lady. "It always stops in Ha'apai. Do you have any hold baggage?"

I placed the first backpack on her weighing scales and watched the display nervously. It flickered between 9 and 14 kilos and settled on 12.4. This satisfied the requirements, and the baggage worker removed it. The second backpack weighed 10.8 kilos. Thank goodness I'd taken the dive regulator out.

I readied myself to step on the scales, but she didn't think we were sufficiently corpulent to warrant this treatment.

Her next words were a bit of a surprise.

"Do you have your cabin baggage?"

Oh no. My hand luggage must have weighed ten kilos with the regulator in it. I lifted it up to show her, trying to make it look as light as I could. Fiona held up the tent, which was her cabin baggage. We knew it weighed four kilos from the label on the side.

"That's fine, here are your boarding passes."

Phew. We walked through the departure area to the gate, which had a sign stating it was gate one. Gate two was on the other side of the room, but no-one was on that side.

"I'm so hot," said Fiona, "this rain jacket weighs a ton."

"It'll be fine to take it off, no more weighing anything."

Chattering, socialising Tongans occupied several seats at the gate. I realised waiting for a flight was another spontaneous engagement in their social calendars. We sat on the floor, and observed them for entertainment.

I looked over at gate two. A heavy chain and padlock sealed its double doors which led outside. Boxes of disinfectant and toilet rolls buried the gate's desk. I didn't think anyone had used gate two for a long time. Possibly for ever.

After a short while the check-in lady appeared. With no microphone available she raised her hands to her mouth and shouted, "flight WR851 now leaving for Vava'u. Please have your boarding passes ready."

≈ ≈ ≈

The red and white plane stood on the tarmac. Printed on its side was the Tongan flag, and large letters advertising Royal Tongan Airlines, with smaller writing noting the make of plane was a De Havilland Otter.

It had seven windows along each side.

It had three wheels.

It had two propellors.

I had seen larger airfix models.

"Are we flying to the Ha'apai Islands in that?" I asked Fiona.

"I hope so, this looks fun."

A young pilot stood at the bottom of the three steps, dressed in a smart crisp white uniform. It appeared tropical against his dark skin.

"May I see your boarding passes please?"

I hesitated. "Now I want to check, we are stopping in Ha'apai, aren't we?"

"We are," said the pilot. "It's pretty rare these days for us to overfly it. In fact, I can't remember the last time we did."

Fiona poked me. "Simon, stop asking everyone where the plane's going. You sound naïve."

We climbed the steps, ducking our heads as we entered the cabin. The seats were arranged in rows of three. My seat was in the front, directly behind the two pilots. Fiona sat on my right, and on the other side my neighbour was a plump middle-aged Tongan nun. Her long heavy brown dress reached down to her sandals. A wooden cross hung round her neck, and she fingered a string of beads.

Nun.

Small plane.

I recalled several airline disaster movies starring Leslie Nielsen, all of which contained nuns.

She addressed me, and I put these thoughts aside.

"Are you going to Ha'apai?"

I omitted the temptation to reply, "I hope so," and simply said "Yes."

"So am I," she said, "I'm going home."

I didn't feel like a long conversation, and I was glad when she pulled out a small leather-bound book and began reading, her lips moving silently.

Is she praying?

Should I be praying?

The pilot climbed on board, closed the door behind him and announced: "Ladies and Gentlemen, welcome to Royal Tongan Airlines flight WR851 to Vava'u…"

My heart paused.

"… via Ha'apai."

I breathed out.

"We will be flying at a height of 9000 feet, and our journey time to Ha'apai will be approximately 30 minutes. Please sit back, relax and enjoy the flight."

≈ ≈ ≈

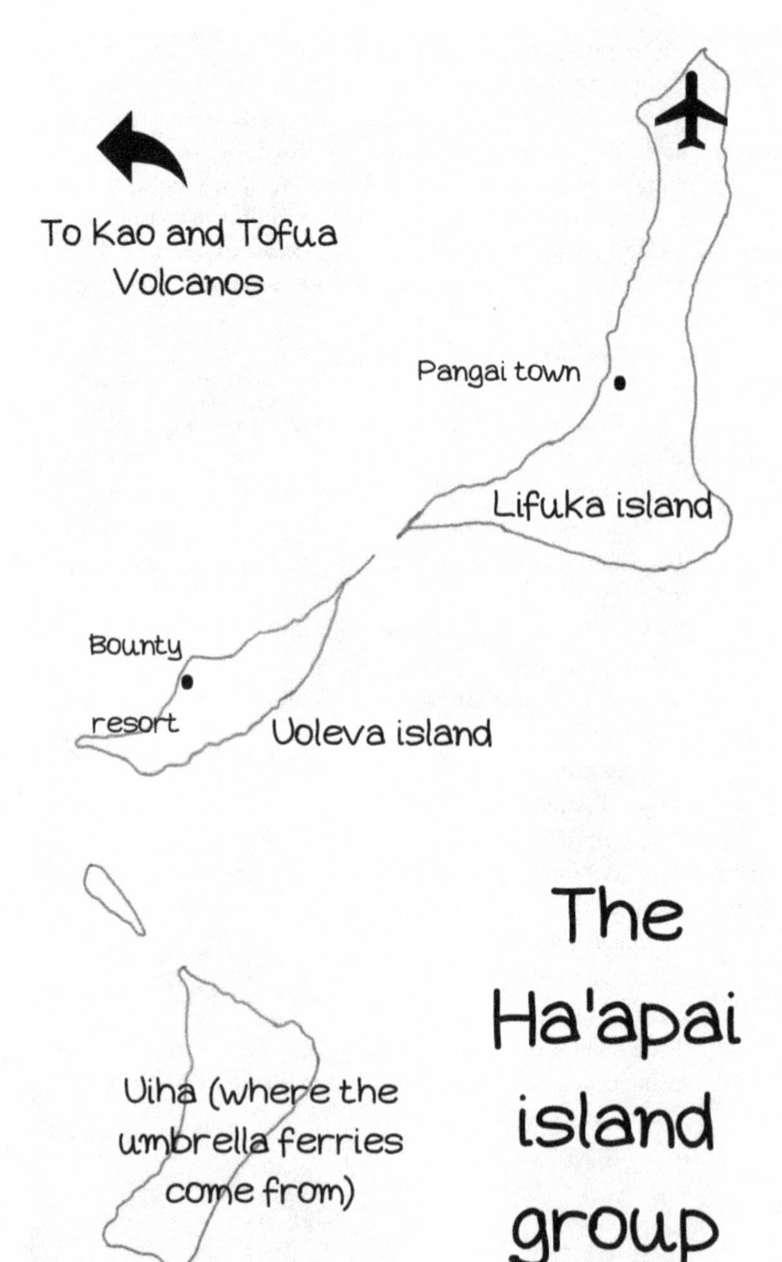
To Kao and Tofua
Volcanos
Pangai town
Lifuka island
Bounty
resort
Uoleva island
Uiha (where the
umbrella ferries
come from)
The
Ha'apai
island
group

The plane vibrated alarmingly as the propellors spun. This was the first time I had flown in a tiny plane, and the different noises made me uneasy. I looked over at Fiona and gave her a nervous smile. If a support group for propellor virgins existed, I was about to become their newest member.

Our plane taxied to the end of the runway and turned round. The increasing noise of the engines preceded sudden acceleration, and in a few seconds we were airborne. It was far too noisy to say anything to Fiona, so I mouthed, "I love you." She gave me a puzzled look and turned towards her window. I had the same view through the windscreen as the pilots, which wasn't an experience available on a 747.

The vista entranced me. Turquoise sea stretched all around us, and I could pick out occasional lighter blue-and-sand-coloured shallow patches. It reminded me of a passage Fiona had read from the guidebook, "Divers fly into Ha'apai looking down in ecstasy." The plane passed over tiny atolls, many with just a small wig of palm trees, the classic children's drawing of a desert island. Nobody could live on such a small piece of land.

Uninhabited desert islands. This is what I've come here for.

After a short while, the note of the engine dropped, and the plane semi-circled.

The nun closed her book.

I looked between the pilots out of the front windscreen in amazement. I could see the runway below us. It wasn't black tarmac; it was light brown dirt. We were approaching fast, and the plane was wobbling violently.

I could see a man jogging along the runway, waving his arms around. What on earth was he doing? Was he an escaped lunatic? Was anyone going to inform him a plane was about to land? Should I tell the pilots, who seemed unaware of him? He was about to be killed by our plane!

25.
The Coconut Wireless

I turned to the nun, and in as calm a voice as I could manage, I asked, "what's that man doing? Why is he on the runway?"

She laughed. "He's the airport manager. Every time a plane arrives, he jumps around waving his arms to scare the pigs away. Then the plane can land safely."

The airport manager.

The pig-scarer.

I decided I was going to like the Ha'apai Islands very much indeed.

≈ ≈ ≈

The plane touched the ground without killing any pigs or airport managers, taxied to the end of the dirt runway, skidded round in a tight semicircle and halted.

"We have arrived, thanks to the Lord," said the nun, placing her book in her bag.

I couldn't have phrased it better myself.

The propellors slowed down.

The engines stopped.

The pilot stepped out of his seat, squeezed past me, and unlatched the door.

Hot air slapped my skin as if I had just opened the oven to remove a Christmas turkey.

"Ladies and Gentlemen," said the pilot, "welcome to the Ha'apai Islands."

I was the first passenger to disembark. I stood at the top of the three steps and gazed at the scene.

Peace.

Quiet.

Complete silence.

"Grunt."

"Grunt grunt grunt."

The pilot shooed a small pig away from the bottom of the steps.

The airport manager, freshly promoted from pig-frightener to baggage attendant, unloaded the bags and cardboard boxes from a hatch near the plane's tail. We collected our backpacks, and turned to follow a track leading away to the edge of the field.

A red Morris Minor with a ladder on its roof and *FIRE* written on the side of it in faded letters stood under a rusty canopy. It had one flat tyre and wasn't best placed to deal with an airport emergency.

"I'm boiling," said Fiona. "I can't wait to take this jacket off. And I need a shower."

"I hope we find somewhere to stay."

"There's a lady with a sign. Can you see what it says?"

"*Hiva's Guest House.* That looks promising."

We approached her.

"Hello," said Fiona, "do you have any room for us?"

"No problem, no problem, come with me."

We followed her a short distance to a brown panel van which had a noticeable list to starboard and a lack of any rear doors. We were glad to divest ourselves of the heavy rain jackets, and placed our bags in the back. There were three seats, one for the driver and two more next to her, so we hopped in. I wondered how she'd have coped if there were any more guests.

"My name is Hiva, welcome to Ha'apai. Are you staying long?"

"I'm Fiona, and this is Simon. We need somewhere to sleep for a couple of nights, then we're going to The Bounty Resort with Kapo Folau."

"Ah, Kapo. He's a naughty boy."

This was an interesting observation.

"Why is he naughty?" asked Fiona.

"He never come to church any Sunday. Tomorrow is Sunday. Today he run away."

I thought back to Tomasi's warning from our conversation in Hawaii, that everyone must go to church on Sunday, and people think badly of you if you miss it.

Hiva started the van's engine by holding two bare wires together, she let in the clutch and gripped the wheel intently.

"Is it okay not to lock your van here?" I asked her.

"No crime here. Everyone very friendly. Also, the van key broke off in the ignition years ago, so I can't lock it even if I needed to."

≈ ≈ ≈

Hiva weaved to the left and right around potholes, as the van meandered along a road which would have benefited from a steamroller. We glimpsed the sea on the right-hand side through dense jungle. No other cars or people troubled the rural scene.

After a few minutes of swerving, we arrived at an inhabited area.

"This is Pangai, capital of the Ha'apai Islands," said Hiva, as she slowed down to allow a large family of dark brown pigs to cross the road.

The houses weren't as well kept as those in Nuku'alofa. Men sat on the front steps and waved as we passed. Hiva waved back. A group of women sat in the shade under a tree. They weren't engaged in anything productive, just silently sitting.

What do they do all day?

We turned off the road on to an unsealed track and arrived at Hiva's guest house. A lady was sweeping the path outside.

"Welcome. I'm Emeni, Hiva's sister."

"My name is Simon, this is Fiona."

"Ahh. Simon. Fiona. You've been staying at Toni's in Nuku'alofa I think?"

"Yes, we have. How did you know that?"

She laughed. "The coconut wireless, of course."

The guest house smelled of fresh paint. Emeni showed us to a large room with four beds in it.

"Thank you," I said, "you've no other guests?"

"No, only you. The room is twelve pa'anga per night. Breakfast is four pa'anga and if you'd like dinner, it's an extra ten pa'anga."

"Sounds perfect," said Fiona, "what are you cooking?"

"Tonight, dinner will be fish with taro and breadfruit."

"I'd like to eat here," I said to Fiona, "it'd be great to experience a home cooked Tongan meal."

"Me too."

"Thank you Emeni, we'd like dinner. Also, can you show us where the showers are?"

"I will, but here in Pangai, we have little water and it only comes on for one hour each day."

"What time can we use them?" asked Fiona.

"Around 5 p.m, I'll turn it on then. Dinner will be at six in the back room."

She departed.

"This is remote, isn't it?" I said. "Pigs running around the streets, water for an hour a day. Shall we go out and explore? Let's try to find Kapo, before he dodges his religious obligations."

≈ ≈ ≈

We opened the front door. It was like being blasted by a supermodel's hair dryer. Emeni still swept the path outside, an activity that engaged her entire day. She poked her broom at three small pigs.

"Whose are all these pigs running around?" asked Fiona, shading her eyes to see Emeni's face.

"Everybody's. They keep trying to eat my vegetables."

"Which way is the boat dock?" I asked. "We need to find Kapo Folau."

"Just head up the road towards the sea. You can't miss it."

We scooted between the odd bits of shade through the tiny town of Pangai. Elderly ladies shuffled along the gravel catwalk dressed in the universally recognisable 'Mediterranean widow' fashion. One waved to us and toothlessly smiled, calling out, "Malo 'e lelei." We returned the greeting.

On the right-hand side of the road, we passed a building called The Free Church of Tonga, which had been painted more exquisitely than Joan Collins's fingernails.

Another institution known as The Church of Jesus Christ of Latter-day Saints occupied a corner near the boat dock. It was as immaculate as a builder's show-home.

"There's a lot of money invested in religion here, isn't there?" I remarked.

"A module of my school project was about that subject," said Fiona. "The churches in Tonga compel people to give them at least ten percent of their income. Believe it or not, they publish a list of people's names in their porch, and next to each name they detail the amount each person has donated. People will do anything to keep off the bottom of the list, even if it means giving more money than they can afford. It's terrible, people here are poor in the first place, and some go without food to avoid the shame of appearing ungenerous with their church donations."

The Church of England collection plate shoved under your nose by the verger at Christmas seemed positively reserved by comparison.

We took advantage of a little shelter that offered some shade, outside the show-home church. Fiona read from a notice board under it.

"Tongan Sunday regulations. Whoever shall do any work on the Sabbath day such as engaging in any trade or sale of any goods or chattels, house-building, boat-building, gardening, fishing, or anything by boat or wagon except in cases of emergency, and whoever shall discharge from the town or country or engage in any game such as cricket, football, lawn tennis, golf, similar games and dancing, *lakalakas, fa'ahiula,* and such like pastimes, shall be liable to a fine not exceeding five pounds or be imprisoned with hard labour for not more than three months for non-payment."

"Wow, you can't do anything on Sunday here, as Tomasi told me. No sport, no gardening, no DIY, nothing. Is that the whole of Sunday I wonder?"

Fiona continued reading, "In this section the term 'Sabbath Day' shall mean the period from twelve midnight Saturday until twelve midnight on the following Sunday."

She paused.

"It's dated 1955," she said, "which would explain the reference to a fine of five pounds. I reckon it's still enforced today."

"I wonder if that applies to us, or just Tongans?"

"We should be careful until we know the score. I don't want to be imprisoned with hard labour for three months."

A small family of pigs crossed the road between us and the dock.

Kapo Folau was absent.

"He must have scarpered already," I said. "Let's go back to the guest house and hide from the heat. We'll come back on Monday."

"All right. I'm getting a bit hungry. If we walk back via the main road, we might find a shop."

A boiling kettle of dust followed a black pickup truck as it passed us. We rubbed our eyes with one hand, waving back at three people riding in the tray.

"Here's a shop of some sort." Fiona pointed at a wooden kiosk. A lady leant out of a hatch in the front, tins and packets displayed either side of her.

"Do you sell bread?" asked Fiona.

"Just rolls. I've four left."

"Do you have anything to put in them?"

"I've tinned meat. Or sliced cheese."

The cheese was from New Zealand, a brand Fiona recognised. We also bought a large bottle of water.

"I'm guessing they don't have a dairy industry here," said Fiona. "The cheese is all this processed sliced rubbish, the milk's in cardboard packets, and I've seen nothing like cream or yoghurt. At least the bread's fresh."

"I reckon most people here grow their own vegetables and keep chickens and pigs."

Dust from the road stuck to our sweat. We were heat-tired as we arrived back at Hiva's.

"I need a shower," said Fiona.

"No water until this evening, remember?"

"Yuck. We're going to have to make sure we take a shower when the water is on. I feel disgusting."

We ate our rolls and cheese on our bed. With no air-conditioning, and a fan that didn't appear to be working, I opened the window to catch the sea breeze. We joined the rest of the Ha'apai Islands population and lay down for a siesta.

≈ ≈ ≈

It was ten past five in the afternoon.

Past five.

Water.

Showers.

"Fiona, wake up."

Fiona sat up suddenly, and rubbed her eyes. "What? What's wrong? I was sooo asleep."

"I know, but it's after 5 p.m. The water will be on."

"Yaaay, cold showers. Time to wash this sweat and dust off."

We threw on T-shirts, grabbed towels, and raced to the showers.

One shower.

With one tap.

Fiona stripped off, jumped into the shower, and turned it on. No water came out.

"I hope we haven't missed it," she said.

"I can hear a tap running in the kitchen," I said. "Stay there and I'll find out."

Hiva was washing vegetables.

"Hi, is there any water for showers? I thought it came on at five?"

"Sorry, sorry. We leave it turned off during the day. We have to be careful with it."

She turned on a tap on the wall. A loud shriek sounded from the bathroom. I concluded that the water was now working.

"It's on now," I shouted to Fiona.

"I know, it's freezing. And it's a funny colour."

The cold water was refreshing, despite its brackish appearance, which mixed with the road dust and disappeared in a yellow-brown sludge down the plughole.

≈ ≈ ≈

The sun set through a small window graced with net curtains, as we sat at the large, square, brown dining table.

"What was for dinner again?" I asked Fiona.

"Fish with taro and breadfruit, traditional Tongan food."

"That's two new items I've never eaten. I've had fish before though."

Hiva appeared with two plates, which she placed in front of us.

Fiona stared at the meal. "Not like this you haven't."

26.
Mosquitos

An entire large brown fish covered my plate. Hiva served Fiona its slightly smaller cousin.

"Freshly caught this afternoon," said Hiva, with pride. "My brother went fishing. Enjoy your dinner."

She departed.

We looked at the fish.

The fish looked back at us.

"Where do you think we start?" I asked, "this isn't exactly cod from Shepherd's Bush chippy."

"Slit the skin, and cut some flesh off both sides of it. It's just white fish."

"I know it is, I'm not used to my dinner gawking at me while I eat it."

I ate a mouthful of fish, cautiously, and tried some of the accompaniments.

"Which is the taro, and which is the breadfruit?" I asked. "They both taste similar. A bit bland."

"Well, this is the food Tongans eat. You wanted to taste Tongan food."

≈ ≈ ≈

Hiva returned. "Did you enjoy your meal?"

The fish stared accusingly at its consumer, the bones of its body still attached to the head.

"You'll have to make dinner yourselves tomorrow; Emeni and I will be out at a church prayer group in the evening. Do you have any food? Everything will be closed as it's Sunday."

Sunday.

Closed.

We had half a packet of biscuits.

Hiva read our faces. "Don't worry, you can have breakfast here. I'll serve it before we go to church. In the evening, the bakery will open after four. The king allowed bakeries to open on Sunday evenings a few years ago, a terrible storm came, and people were starving. But they only sell bread, nothing else."

"Thank you," I said, "that's a relief."

"Will you be coming to church tomorrow? You can come with us if you like."

"We're going to the Wesleyan one. We want to hear the band."

"That band will have been practising hard," said Hiva. "The king is coming next week."

"Do you think the queen will be with him?" I asked. "I really want to see her; it's the main reason we travelled to Tonga."

"Sometimes they're together, sometimes not. We won't know until they arrive. See you tomorrow. Breakfast will be at eight. Sleep well."

≈ ≈ ≈

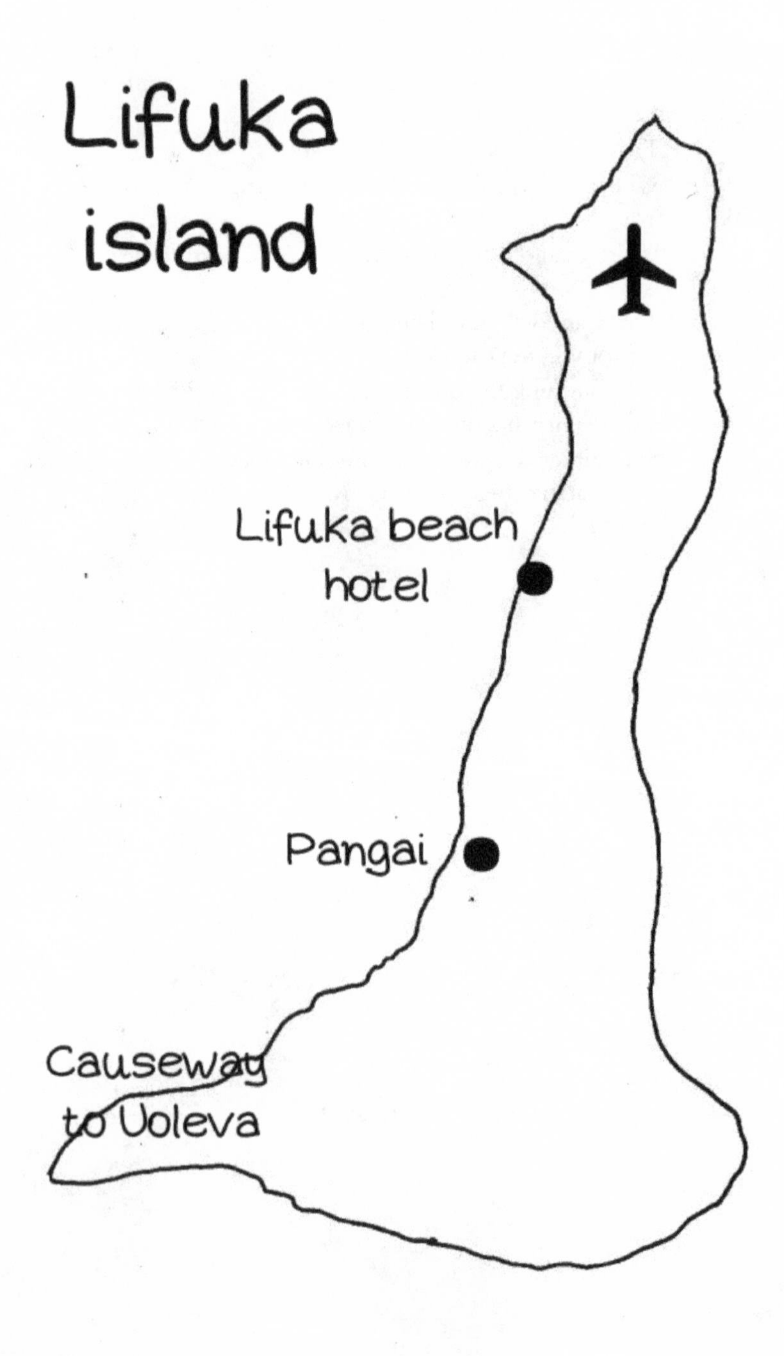
Lifuka
island
Lifuka beach
hotel
Pangai
Causeway
to Uoleva

The lights in the hallway flickered and dimmed as we opened our bedroom door.

The room was full of mosquitos.

"Who left the window open?" asked Fiona, "close it for goodness sake."

She found two cans of bug killer, and sprayed them around the room. Within seconds thousands of insects were lying on their backs waving their legs in the air, and I was about to join them.

"Did you have to spray so much? I can't breathe. Open the window, I need air."

"I can't open the window; the bugs will come back in."

"I'll never be able to sleep without the window open," I said, "it's boiling in here. I wish we had something to protect us from all the insects."

"What about our mosquito net?"

Mosquito net.

I completely forgot we brought a mosquito net.

"Great thinking. Let's pin it up over the bed, spray some more mossie killer around, open the window, and quickly jump under it."

We lay inside the protection of the mosquito net, a sea of tranquillity within a world of gigantic people-eating flying creatures, waiting to pounce on our virgin skin.

"I need the toilet," said Fiona.

"Oh no. How are you going to climb out without the mosquitos getting in?"

"Give me the cans of spray."

Fiona unzipped the mosquito net, raised the two cans in front of her, and like Rambo exiting his lair, she sprayed her weapons from left to right letting the insects have it with both barrels. I zipped the net up behind her, my eyes stinging.

"Try not to let too many in when you return," I said.

While Fiona was out of the room, I dipped into the travel guide.

Ha'apai, it confirmed, was a deeply religious group of islands. There were no less than twelve churches in Pangai alone, for a population of 2000. Christianity had come late to Tonga, in

1831, when a chief called Taufa'ahau was baptised, and took the name of King George I. Prior to this, Ha'apai claimed notoriety as the location where the *Mutiny on the Bou*nty had occurred.

In 1789, a few miles off the coast of a volcanic island called Tofua, mutineers led by a man named Fletcher Christian took control of the *Bounty* from Captain William Bligh, and threw him and eighteen other crew into a small boat, pushing them away to an unknown fate. Christian had his own challenges, upon landing on Tofua, the Tongans attacked him and his fellow mutineers, and they had to sail away quickly before they became lunch.

I realised this must be why Kapo Folau had named his island 'The Bounty Resort.'

Captain Cook had almost met the same fate twelve years earlier, explained the guide. A local Ha'apai chief invited him and his men to a feast in their honour. The amount of food on offer impressed James Cook, and the beautiful dancing entranced him. He seemed unaware he and his men were destined to become the main course. History relates the chief argued with other important Tongans about how to entice Cook to climb into the pot, and Cook departed, naming Tonga *The Friendly Isles*. He remained forever ignorant that he'd almost been the victim of cannibalism.

I recalled the giant cooking pot we'd seen at the Tongan National Centre and wondered if this was the one they had tried to boil Captain Cook in.

Fiona returned from the bathroom, unzipped the net and jumped back on the bed. 1000 mosquitos followed her, and she unleashed a further blanket of napalm.

"We should take a photo of ourselves lying on the bed under the mosquito net," she said. "This'll be a memory for the future."

"Good idea." I set the self-timer on the camera and propped it up facing in our direction. We both smiled.

The camera flashed and clicked. The click sounded different to its normal picture-taking sound. I turned it over and looked at the little screen.

"Oh no."

"What's wrong, Simon?"

"You know how I was really organised and brought ten films with us, as I wasn't sure you'd be able to buy them here?"

"Yeeeessss…."

"What do you reckon the chances are of being able to buy a new battery for an Olympus Infinity Stylus?"

"None whatsoever."

"I'm so stupid. I forgot to bring a spare battery. It hasn't needed changing in years. Now we can't take any pictures."

"You still have those disposable cameras you use for snorkelling."

"I've only brought two of them. That's 48 photos. We're going to have to ration our photography."

We lay on the bed. In the distance, we could hear church choirs rehearsing for Sunday, accompanied by brass bands.

Closer to the guest house, pig choirs also practised for their forthcoming concert. Occasionally, a soprano or contralto dog sang a guest aria. These ensembles weren't as harmonic, and their songs were rather repetitive, with the occasional pause to fool you into thinking they'd finished.

"Do these pigs ever go to sleep?" asked Fiona.

"I think they finish their shift at dawn and hand over to the chickens."

≈ ≈ ≈

We were already hot as the sun streamed in at nine o'clock. Fiona opened the mosquito net zip, her cans of spray ready to deliver further carpet-bombing.

"Simon, the mosquitos have gone. There are none coming in."

"I'm sure they'll be back this evening."

"I'm going to the bathroom. Back in a mo."

Fiona pulled on a T-shirt and left. I lay on the bed, immobile in the heat.

In the distance I could hear another church choir. I remembered it was Sunday. The singing was angelic; it was a pleasure to lie there and just listen.

I consulted the guidebook; I wanted to make sure we wore the correct attire to church.

'When visiting a church or cultural site, men are required to wear a shirt. This includes tourists. A fine of twenty pa'anga is payable for a breach of this regulation. Women must cover their shoulders and chests and their legs to the knees. A woman who disregards this rule risks being thought of as promiscuous.'

It was lucky Fiona had bought those long dresses in Hawaii.

She returned, banging the door.

"Ssssshhh," I said, "listen."

"Yup, pigs and chickens are busy again."

"No, listen to the church choir. It's beautiful."

"Very nice. Hiva's laid out breakfast in the dining room. We should go."

I hopped through the mosquito net and pulled out my Hawaiian shirt. It was the smartest thing I owned.

Fiona selected a pair of shorts and tugged them on.

"Errr you look good," I said, "but you probably shouldn't wear the shorts to church."

"Don't you like these shorts, Simon?"

"Yes, but the guide says women have to cover up their legs in church or they may be mistaken for prostitutes. I'm fairly sure that's what it said."

"Seriously? Okay, I don't want anyone to think I'm selling my body. I'll change into a long dress."

Breakfast consisted of cornflakes (more Sanitarium!) with bread and fresh fruit and a hard-boiled egg.

"This papaya is amazing," said Fiona, juice running down her chin. "I love these tropical fruits."

"We'd better eat as much as possible; lunch is half a packet of biscuits and dinner is a loaf of bread from the bakery."

"Have you cut your egg open yet? The yolk is orange; the pale-yellow ones we buy from the supermarket seem artificial next to these. I could almost forgive the chickens for their pok-pok-pokking."

"We'd better hurry. Church starts at ten."

The quiet streets contained men wearing smart black dress shirts and brown woven mats on their bottom halves, which gave the appearance they had skirts on. Ladies wore full-length summer dresses. Everyone was going to morning worship.

"I'm a bit nervous we won't know what to do at the service," I said.

"I'm sure we'll be fine. Copy the locals."

≈ ≈ ≈

A towering painting of Jesus gazed upon us from behind the altar, under a ceiling adorned with a huge pink cross. Small windows set high above our heads allowed tiny slivers of sunlight to enter and reflect off the white walls.

Fiona shivered.

"You can't be cold?" I asked her.

"I wish I'd brought a jumper. I'll acclimatise."

Nobody was handing out prayer books or other literature, not that we could have read the Tongan.

We sat down on a dark wooden pew near the back. Other people arrived and took their seats quietly, and by 10 a.m. the church was full. Many latecomers were standing.

"Gosh," I said to Fiona, "if it's this busy today, how many will be here next week when the king comes? It'll be like *Songs of Praise.*

"Sssssh, the choir's entering. And the band."

About 100 men, boys and girls wearing white uniforms filed in, some carrying sheets of paper, some carrying instruments. Tomasi must have been among them, but there were a lot of band members and I couldn't see him.

The choirmaster took his position behind a small lectern. I expected him to raise his baton, but he stood in silence.

What are we waiting for?

27.
The Prime Minister in the Cemetery

A priest stood up and cleared his throat. He read a brief passage aloud in Tongan. When he'd finished, the choir and congregation sang a few lines. Then the priest read another verse. The singers followed him again.

Fiona leant towards me and whispered, "They're repeating what he's saying. He reads a verse of a hymn, then they sing it. He reads another verse, and they sing that."

"There's something in the back of my mind telling me they used to do this repetition thing in England in Victorian days. Something to do with people being illiterate, they sang one verse at a time, so people could remember the words. I bet this is a hangover from that period."

The singing from both the choir and congregation rivalled any harmonies a Welsh miners' ensemble could have produced.

The alternately spoken and sung hymn finished. Some Bible passages in Tongan followed, and the band leader stood up and raised his baton. A pause of expectant silence, then the sudden first notes of the English Christmas favourite *God Rest ye Merry Gentlemen.*

"I know this one." I said, humming hopelessly out of tune.

"Ssshhh, people haven't come to hear you."

The band continued with a medley of Christmas carols, all of which were familiar. The band leader had probably written the arrangement himself.

He vacated the lectern, and the priest ascended a few steps into the wooden pulpit.

"I hope his speech isn't too long," I whispered to Fiona, "these seats aren't very comfortable."

The priest cleared his throat again.

He addressed the crowd in a deep, slow voice.

In Tongan.

≈ ≈ ≈

After a few minutes I shuffled in my seat. Sermons weren't my favourite auditory pleasure in my own language; the foreign tongue made concentrating as hard as listening to paint dry.

The preacher continued his monotone prose.

I gazed around the church at the attentive congregation. At one point there was a loud murmur. Clearly the priest had said something that resonated with his flock. He could have been sharing a chocolate chip cookie recipe for all I understood.

Twenty minutes after he'd begun, he sat down. The choir and band stood up again.

"Well, that's twenty minutes of my life I'll never get back."

"Stop complaining, Simon. This is an experience most people never have."

A further two hymns followed, continuing the pattern of spoken words echoed by sung stanzas. The singing was ethereal, magnificent. Every Tongan must leave the womb with a voice like Kiri Te Kanawa.

The priest stood in front of the congregation and intoned what I took to be some closing words. He looked directly at me and said in perfect English, "To our guests from overseas, thank you for coming, we hope to see you again soon."

I smiled and raised my hand. Fiona looked embarrassed and shrank down in her seat.

The service had ended.

≈ ≈ ≈

Outside the church, people hugged and kissed each other, men shook hands, children ran round in circles, dressed in miniature versions of their parents' outfits.

A large man wearing a black shirt with a mat around his waist greeted us.

"Welcome," he said. "How long will you be staying? Will you be here next weekend?"

"We will," I said, "we're in Ha'apai for two weeks."

"Oh, that's wonderful. Next weekend the king will be here. On the Saturday evening, there will be a feast and celebration for the entire island. I want you both to come as my guests."

This wasn't a request. We'd be rude to refuse; a Tongan feast was an event not to miss.

I made a mental note to fast for several days beforehand.

"Thank you, it would honour us to come," I said, rather formally.

Tomasi ran up to us, holding his trumpet. "Hello you two, you made it to Ha'apai. And you've met my Uncle Mafu."

"Tomasi, your band is amazing," Fiona said, "it's no wonder you did so well in the Pacific music competition."

"Thank you, we've been practising hard; it has to be right for the king."

Uncle Mafu spoke. "Tomasi, I was inviting our guests to the feast next week. Can I count on you to keep them company? I may be busy helping entertain the king."

"Of course. I was going to invite them myself."

"Excuse me, Uncle Mafu," I asked, "Everyone keeps talking about the king, and we're excited that he's coming, but do you know if the queen will be here? I'm on a bit of a mission to catch sight of her. My father was so enthusiastic about seeing the last queen, and I would love to catch a glimpse of the current one."

"Ah, Queen Sālote, she attended Queen Elizabeth of England's coronation. I saw her myself when I was a small boy. She was a kind lady, and all of Tonga loved her."

"That's where my father spotted her, at the coronation. He told me a story about how she smiled and waved at him. I wish she were still alive."

"The current royal couple spend a lot of time in New Zealand," said Uncle Mafu. "They've a home in Auckland. Sometimes they travel together, sometimes separately. We hope they'll both come to the Ha'apai Islands, but we won't know until they're here."

"I have to go," said Tomasi, "I'll see you both at the feast next week. It's at the rugby field. Meet me in the afternoon. It'll be so exciting."

He ran back to join the members of his band, and Uncle Mafu turned away to talk to some other men.

"Shall we go back to the guest house?" asked Fiona, "It's too hot to be out in the sun."

≈ ≈ ≈

We sprawled under the mosquito net and ate our ration of half a packet of gingernut biscuits, sharing them out equally and carefully breaking the last one in half.

"I can't wait until the bakery opens," I said, "I'm so hungry. We need to plan better for this Sunday closing. What can we do to keep our minds off food?"

"Well, the guide suggests visiting the grave of Shirley Baker, from London, who became the Prime Minister of Tonga back in the 1880s."

"Shirley? Wow, the Tongans were progressive. Britain didn't have a female Prime Minister until Margaret Thatcher."

Fiona laughed. "Despite the name, Simon, he was a man."

"Maybe his parents wanted a daughter?"

Fiona ignored my quip. "He designed the Tongan flag, national anthem and constitution. He was responsible for Tonga becoming more like the nation it is today."

"Okay, we'll pay him a visit."

"Then up the road from the cemetery there's the dive school you wanted to check out. Shall we drop in and investigate if they're running trips?"

"Sounds like a plan."

"I hope the showers are on when we return," said Fiona, "I'm sick of dripping in sweat."

≈ ≈ ≈

Groups of pigs slept in the shade of bushes at the side of the main road, their ears twitching at passing flies. The distant backdrop of choral music broke the afternoon silence, and the hairdryer breeze blew uncomfortably, as we strolled up the main road, following the route back towards the airport.

A life-size monument of Shirley Baker raised high on a plinth dominated his grave. The sculptor had portrayed him as a great statesman, a stern, solid Englishman with huge sideburns, leaning on a post, holding a scroll. Traditional western headstones, the resting places of missionaries and other long-deceased Europeans who'd ended their lives on these shores surrounded him, a Cotswold country churchyard amongst the palm trees.

On the opposite side of the road, we found another cemetery where the native Tongans buried their dead. Small sand dunes formed the graves, and jam jars contained complicated arrangements of plastic flowers. Around the edges of the dunes, shells, old Coke cans and empty beer bottles decorated the graves.

"I wonder if they represent what the deceased liked to drink?" I asked. "It'd have been expensive if he'd liked Champagne."

Fiona laughed, "… or whisky. It's amazing how different cultures commemorate their dead. You can learn a lot about a nation from their graveyards."

Sweat ran down her bright red face.

"Come on," I said, taking her hand, "let's walk up the beach. The dive school must be by the sea."

The shade of the palms offered some relief. Plastic containers, multi-coloured packets, cans and bottles festooned the shore in a long wiggly line parallel to the breaking waves.

"Why don't the Tongans put their litter in the bin?" I asked.

"This all came from somewhere else, I'm sure. The sea's washed it here, but there's no-one to clean it up."

"It's sad, isn't it? Rubbish in paradise."

"Is that the dive school up ahead?" asked Fiona.

"It's a big one if it is."

A basic communal reception area surrounded by small huts was situated right on the sand. There was no indication anyone worked there. A sign said: *Lifuka Beach Hotel.*

"Shall we ask if we can stay here when we come back from The Bounty Resort?" Fiona asked. "Their showers might be more reliable."

≈ ≈ ≈

A large elderly Tongan lady sat in a beach chair outside reception. She was the only human we'd seen since leaving Pangai.

I approached her. "Malo 'e leilei, we're looking for somewhere to stay in a week's time. Do you have room?"

"Plenty of room for you, and we have food too. If you come and stay here with me, I'll give you free breakfast and half-price dinner."

That sounded good. I was so hungry I wanted to ask for it in advance.

"All right, we'll come back in a week. Thank you."

The dive school was next to the hotel. A sign on its door said, *back in ten minutes*.

We sat on the beach and waited ten minutes. Nobody came, so we waited another ten to make sure. Still nobody came. I reckoned the sign was there all day.

≈ ≈ ≈

Fiona stood naked in the guest house shower and turned the tap, but nothing came out.

"This is ridiculous," she said, "where's Hiva and Emeni?"

"I don't think anyone's home. They must be at church."

"Far out. I'm so sweaty. And we've run out of bottled water. This isn't good."

"Let's walk over to the bakery. It'll be open by now. Maybe the ladies will have returned by the time we come back."

The bakery was next to the rugby field. Fiona tried the locked door.

"It's well after 4 p.m.," she said. "Why aren't they open?"

"They're probably late, this is Tonga. We'll have to wait."

A lady walked up to the shop and disappeared behind it. She came back carrying some bread.

"Malo 'e leilei," she said, "are you waiting for the bakery? You go to the back door on Sundays. The law allows them to open, but they don't advertise it."

The back door to the bakery was ajar, and Fiona poked her nose inside the dark room.

"A loaf of bread, please, and do you have anything to drink?"

An unseen voice responded, "I've some bottles of water, but I'm not supposed to sell them today. Give me your bag."

Fiona handed over her day pack and the voice returned it a lot heavier. She paid the invisible baker.

We ate our bread and drank our water in our bedroom. The showers were still off.

"I don't mind roughing it," I said, "but dinner of bread and water and no showers all day is taking things a bit far. I hope the other hotel is better. It looks it."

"Let's find Kapo tomorrow. I wish I were a cat, then I could just lick myself clean."

≈ ≈ ≈

It was morning.

Monday morning.

The shopping abstinence of Sunday had ended.

"Come on Fiona, let's eat breakfast and get out of here. It's time to find Kapo and start our desert island lives."

"Shower first? I feel disgusting."

"We'll ask at breakfast."

We were ravenous after the paucity of the previous day's offerings and we stuffed ourselves with the beautiful fresh fruit, fresh bread and eggs.

"Hiva, can you turn the water on this morning?" Fiona asked, "there weren't any showers yesterday."

"Sorry, sorry, we were out at church. Let me try."

She disappeared to the kitchen, and we heard a creaky tap being turned, followed by water coming out in short sharp spurts.

"There is a bit of water," said Hiva, "but it's not a very nice colour."

"I don't care what colour it is," said Fiona, "I'm having a shower."

"You'd better be quick," said Hiva, "there isn't any in the mornings usually."

We dashed to grab towels and washbags.

Fiona stripped off and jumped in the shower. A trickle of brown water ran over her like yesterday's gravy.

"Leave some for me."

"I'm not sure there's enough, Simon."

She was drying off after 30 seconds. I hopped in and turned the tap.

Nothing.

No water.

Not even a trickle of Bisto.

"Thanks. I would have liked a shower too," I said.

"I don't know when we're going to find one now, there's no running water on Bounty Island, is there?"

"They must have something if people stay for days on end."

We threw on some clothes, packed up our bags and left the drought of Hiva's Guest House, one of us considerably more fragrant than the other.

≈ ≈ ≈

Our feet scrunched on the gravel as we route-marched to the boat harbour. Unpleasant large sweaty patches formed between our T-shirts and our backpacks.

People smiled and called out *Malo 'e leilei.* We were conspicuously the only tourists in town today, but we weren't the first they'd ever seen.

Two small wooden blue-and-white boats bobbed pleasantly against the wharf. A man sat on the edge of one, mending a fishing net.

"Hello," I said, "we're looking for Kapo Folau. Do you know him?"

The man laughed. "Everyone knows Kapo. He disappears to his island every weekend, so he doesn't have to go to church. He'll be here soon; he returns every Monday morning to fetch supplies."

"Thank you, we'll wait for him."

As we were familiar with the Tongan definition of 'soon,' we dumped the packs and lay down in the shade of a tree. Fiona propped herself up against her bag and pulled out the guidebook.

I reflected on how remote from civilisation we were. We were on a tiny island, a 30-minute flight from anything that we could call a town, and thousands of miles from the nearest city. And we were about to travel to a tinier island, a desert island no less. I felt a massive sense of achievement. All that remained was to find the Queen of Tonga and my travel goals would be complete. I thought back to the conversation with my father, our unplanned trip to Paris, all the preparation we'd done for the journey, working at the steam fair, my redundancy, Ben the travel agent….

A short stocky man stood over me, staring in my face. I had fallen asleep in the heat.

"Excuse me, were you looking for me?" he said.

"Kapo?" My foot had gone to sleep, and I pushed myself up and staggered around on one leg like a man limping home from the pub.

"I'm Kapo, did you want to stay on my island?"

I stuck my hand in the front pocket of my pack and discarded tickets, brochures, passports and stubs of old boarding passes around the base of the tree. Kapo waited patiently.

"Found it. Here." I handed him the letter he'd written to me months ago.

Kapo took the letter and read it, recognising his own handwriting. He pointed at the words in amazement, showing them back to me.

"And this is you?"

"This is indeed me."

"Wonderful, wonderful," he said, as if he'd been waiting for my arrival all his life. "I'm going shopping here, then I'll return to the island at lunchtime and you can come with me on my boat. How long do you want to stay?"

"Mmm, maybe five nights? We need to be back in Pangai by the weekend as we're going to a feast."

"No problem. Make sure you've enough food with you. You can put your bags on the boat while you go shopping if you like."

Fiona stood up and joined us, and we carried the backpacks to his small wooden craft. We dumped them on his deck gratefully. It was too hot to lug them around.

"See you in an hour," Kapo said, and he walked off towards the town.

"I was reading in the guidebook about Kapo's island," said Fiona. "We're going to be staying on one of the most beautiful beaches in Tonga."

"Wow, I can't wait. We need to do a quick bit of food shopping. Plus, we must go to the bank and change some more travellers cheques; we've no cash and we'll need some to pay Kapo."

"Is Kapo taking us to the island?"

"Yep, he's getting some shopping as well and we'll meet him back at the boat."

We bought some tins and packets of food. Fresh food would have been nicer, but we knew there was no electricity on his island so there wouldn't be a fridge. Kapo wasn't in the shop.

When we returned to the boat, he was already waiting, and we discovered his purchases were quite different to ours.

His shopping didn't need a fridge either.

It wasn't tins and packets.

It was alive.

28.
The Bounty Girl

We sat either side of the centre engine box in Kapo's small open boat. He perched at the stern, cross-legged, one hand on the tiller. In the bow of the boat Kapo had placed his shopping, two small brown piglets which snuffled around, falling over each other like a pair of miniature wrestlers.

The pigs infatuated Fiona. "Oh, they're so cute. Aren't you the cutest things, little piggies?"

"Don't get too attached to them," I said, "I don't think they're pets."

Twenty minutes later we rounded the top corner of Kapo's island, and he slowed the boat and stood up, looking over the side.

"I'm watching out for the coral heads," he said, "I don't want to hit one."

Huge brain-shaped brown masses loomed just under the surface of the water, surrounded by tiny fish.

"Fiona, it's so clear; you can see right to the bottom. It's an aquarium, I'm glad we brought our snorkels."

"And look, look at the beach," said Fiona, "I'm in a travel brochure."

Under the swaying palm trees, four figures stood on the shore. One of them broke away from the group and held his hand to his eyes to shield the reflection from the jewelled white sand, shimmering with tiny points of light. He walked through the tiny wavelets towards us, naked except for cut off denim shorts, bronzed skin with sun-bleached long blonde hair. He stood in the sea up to his knees, watching our approach, his hands on his hips.

Fiona was right. We were in a travel brochure. One of the brochures you're embarrassed to ask the travel agent for, because both of you know you can't afford anything in it.

Kapo dropped the anchor in the shallows and cut the engine.

"We walk from here," he said.

"We do?"

"Hold your bags over your heads." He grabbed a piglet under each arm and jumped over the side, wading on to the beach. We followed, carrying our backpacks. The sea was the temperature of a baby's bottle. Warmer than the guest house showers.

We're here.

On a desert island.

We'd never be more remote from civilisation in our lives.

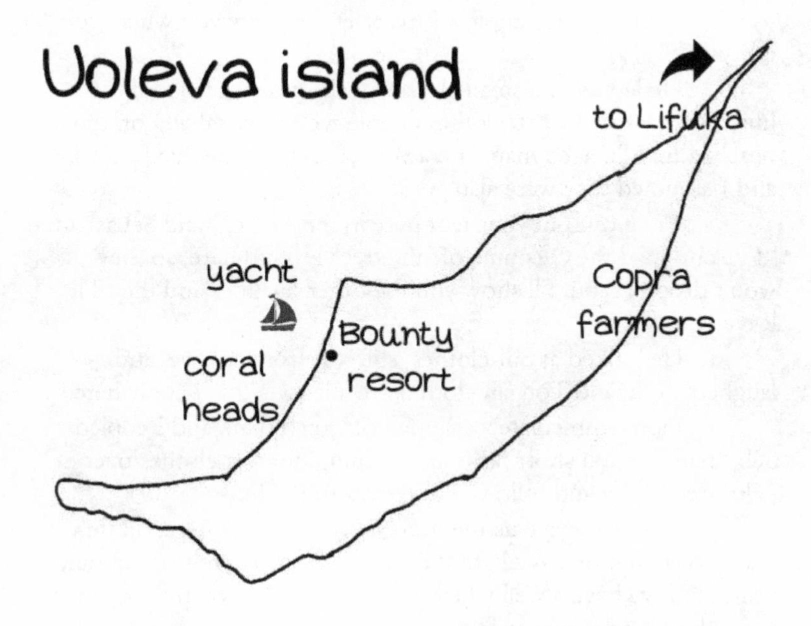

I dumped my backpack and surveyed the scene, dripping warm water from my wet shorts. Two small huts stood among some palm trees in front of the impenetrable jungle. A red dinghy rested on the sand, just out of the water. A short distance offshore a sailing yacht lay at anchor, its tall mast rocking left and right rhythmically like a floating metronome.

On the horizon, heat haze blurred the faint outlines of Kao and Tofua, the twin volcanoes. Kao was a children's drawing of a volcano, a perfect isosceles triangle. I knew the flatter island of

Tofua was still active. It was where the Mutiny on the Bounty had occurred, all those centuries ago.

The tanned observer introduced himself.

"Hi, I'm Sebastian. I live here with Kapo. Are you two together? We're a bit short on sleeping space, and there's only one bed left."

"I'm Simon, this is Fiona, and we're definitely together. We're okay for beds, we brought our own tent."

"Oh, you're camping. Great, let me show you where you can put it."

He led us to a small clearing a short distance from the huts. We passed the three other people who were talking on the beach, a middle-aged man, and a young couple. The man waved, and I assumed they were also guests.

"You can put your tent here in the shade," said Sebastian. "I've chopped the coconuts off the trees around here, so they won't drop on you. I'll show you the other facilities and then I'll leave you to it."

He looked at our clothes, still wet from the sea, and laughed. "Oh, and Tongan clothing regulations don't apply here."

Fiona immediately stripped off to a bikini, and I copied Sebastian's denim short fashion. We hung our wet clothes over a palm tree to dry and followed him over to the huts.

Sebastian gave us the tour. "You can cook here, on this grate above the fire. We light it every evening. There's no running water, but we have a well which is safe to drink. You pull on this rope, there's a jug on the end."

He demonstrated use of the well by heaving up a jug full of water. It seemed a straightforward process.

"What about showers?" asked Fiona.

"Oh, you're going to love our showers, let me show you."

Woven palm leaves attached to upright tree trunks formed an open-air three-sided cubicle. The entrance faced into the jungle.

"You scoop jugs of water from the well and fill up this bowl." Sebastian pointed to a large, shallow, metal container. "You stand in here and tip the water over yourself with this."

A cut-in-half Schweppes lemonade bottle hung on the end of a piece of string.

"I think," said Fiona, "we'll be considerably cleaner than we were in town."

"Come and meet the others," said Sebastian.

We followed Sebastian over to the group on the beach.

A man of around 50 years old smiled at us from under his big brown moustache. His floppy hat and open short-sleeved shirt protected him from the sun.

"Hi, I'm Mark. That's my boat."

He pointed at the yacht anchored offshore, pronouncing the word as *boot.*

"Simon and Fiona," I said, "pleased to meet you."

"I think you're from Canada?" Fiona picked up on his accent.

"I am, we've sailed here from Vancouver. We arrived this morning."

He introduced us to the young couple with him.

"This is Johnny and Ingrid, they're my crew. Guys, this is Simon and Fiona."

Johnny also subscribed to the denim shorts fashion. He had wavy black hair and his skin was dark brown from weeks spent working on the deck of the yacht.

He held out his hand for me to shake. "Hey Simon, and Fiona is it?"

He had a friendly American accent.

Ingrid gave a brief fake smile, her eyes invisible behind expensive sunglasses. I disliked her instantly. She wasn't pretty, but she had a model's body, with long brown hair and bronzed skin, the essential bits covered confidently by a micro-bikini. She looked good, and she knew it. Her entire voyage had consisted of sunbathing, while Mark and Johnny did all the hard work.

"Johnny and Ingrid are leaving me here in Tonga, I'm a bit stuck until I find someone else." Mark looked at us hopefully.

"We've been sailing since June," said Johnny, "we need a break from it; we're staying here on dry land."

"Anyway, good to meet you," said Mark. "I'll catch you all later on; I've got some maintenance to do." He hopped into the red dinghy we'd seen, pushed it away from the land and started the tiny outboard motor. We watched him putter to the yacht.

Sebastian led Johnny and Ingrid over to the huts, leaving us standing on the sand.

"Shall we put the tent up and explore?" Fiona asked.

≈ ≈ ≈

Our two-person tent didn't take long to erect; the procedure benefited from many rehearsals. It was the first purchase Fiona and I had made as a couple and we'd enjoyed many camping trips with it.

"This will be the most incredible view to wake up to. Let's test it out," said Fiona.

We lay in the tent on our stomachs, looking out over the water.

It was beautiful, but inside, the temperature was already hot enough to melt steel girders.

"I don't think we're ever going to be able to lie in the tent during the day," I said, "I think I've lost about four pints of sweat. Let's go and investigate the shower."

We grabbed towels and washbags and walked over to the cubicle.

"Right, let's see if I can remember this," I said. "We take this shallow bowl over to the well and fill it up from the jug on the end of the rope. We bring it back and tip water over ourselves with the plastic bottle."

The jug dropped down the well, and a splash echoed from a long way below. I pulled the rope up and the jug reappeared. It was one quarter full.

I emptied the jug into the bowl and dropped it again. The same thing happened.

"There must be a technique to getting the jug to fill up," I said, "it's going to take ages at this rate."

Multiple jug-drops later my shoulders were aching.

"Is that enough?" I asked Fiona.

"I should think so. You could always fetch me some more."

We carried the bowl between us to the shower, trying not to spill any, and placed it on a shelf inside the cubicle.

"Simon, can you keep watch to make sure no-one comes?"

Fiona stripped off her bikini and hung it on a nearby palm tree. She scooped up some water with the half-bottle and tipped it over herself.

"Brrrrrr, this is much colder than the sea was."

She sploshed some more water and soaped herself until suds and shampoo covered her.

"Quick," I said, "someone's coming."

"Well tell them to go away," said Fiona, grabbing the half lemonade bottle and tipping it over herself several times.

"Only joking, no-one's around."

"I," said Fiona as she rubbed her face with her towel, "I'm going to get you for that."

She threw a half-bottle of cold water over me.

"That's freezing!"

"Yes, and that was the last of the water. You'll have to fill the bowl up again. Serves you right for frightening me."

She wrapped her towel around herself, picked up her bikini and marched off to the tent.

"Hey," I shouted after her, "what about keeping watch for me?"

"What about it?" she called back over her shoulder.

I quarter-filled the bowl from the well again and carried it back to the shower.

When I returned to the tent, I found Fiona sitting on the sand with a book. She had wrapped a blue patterned sarong tightly around her top half which left her sun-kissed shoulders exposed. She had found a large red flower and had stuck it behind her ear.

She looks like the girl from the Bounty chocolate advertisement; I hope she isn't still mad at me.

"Have a nice shower?" she asked, "did anyone see you?"

"Most amusing."

Near the huts we found two hammocks. A pair of dogs were sleeping under a tree close by, and took no notice of us. The piglets were rolling around playing in the sand.

"They're so sweet," said Fiona, "is someone really going to eat them?"

"I'm sure that won't happen while we're here. Pretend they're pets for the moment."

Fiona picked one up, and it squealed like a deflating balloon. The dogs raised their heads, looked around, and returned to their siesta. Fiona placed the pig down.

"I'm not sure they're used to being held," I said. "Try patting it on the ground."

Fiona scratched the piglet behind its ears, which it preferred. Its sibling had found a small coconut, and it was trying to fit the whole thing into its mouth. We hopped into the hammocks and swung gently under the trees.

"This is absolute paradise." I closed my eyes.

"What's for lunch?" asked Fiona.

"I'm not hungry in this heat. What do we have that's not too filling?"

"Biscuits? I'll go and fetch them."

We lay in the hammocks, eating our biscuits and drinking water from bottles. I experimented and found by pushing off a tree stump I could make the hammock swing slowly back and forth, back and forth.

Warm sun.

Gently lapping sea.

Rocking hammock.

Breeze in the trees.

"I'm bored," said Fiona. "There's nothing to do here."

"Isn't that the idea? Come on then, let's go for a stroll up the beach."

We fell out of the hammocks and stood up. Sebastian and Johnny conversed at a wooden bench. Ingrid lay a short distance away on the beach, reading a magazine.

≈ ≈ ≈

The piglets followed us, but failed to keep up, and we abandoned them to the distraction of a large crab. A long squeak indicated the crab had won the first round.

I drank in the experience of walking down the deserted pure white seashore, feeling guilty for messing up the perfect sand. With no-one in front of us, and behind us only our trail of footprints, this was the epitome of tourist brochures, yet no tourist would ever witness this. The experience was reserved for travellers such as us, who didn't mind camping somewhere with no facilities.

"Imagine if mass tourism ever arrived; this place would be desecrated," I said. "But the ironic thing is, this is what all those tourists who go to Waikiki are looking for."

"The shopping's better in Waikiki; you won't be able to buy a Hawaiian shirt here."

"I don't think, while I'm on this island, I'm going to wear a shirt at all. Sebastian seems to have the dress code sorted out."

"I know," said Fiona, "I looked at the three of you all wearing your denim shorts and wondered if I hadn't received the memo."

"Well, Kapo wears trousers. Come to think of it, Tongans don't wear shorts. They either wear long trousers or those woven mats like the men at church."

Large, complex shells were scattered over the sand; we collected some and arranged them in a pattern.

"Let's take a photo of these," said Fiona, "people back home won't have seen shells this big. This conch is enormous."

"How will we be able to show how big they are in the photo? We need something for scale. Hang on, I've found a penknife in my pocket."

We photographed the shells alongside the knife. One of the shells got up and ran away.

Fiona had the giggles. "You need to check there aren't any hermit crabs in them first."

Two more shells started to move.

"I'm glad they stayed still for their family photo," she said.

In the edge of our vision, something significantly bigger than a crab ran across the beach ahead of us and disappeared into a hole.

Fiona grabbed my hand. "Did you see that?"

29.
Desert Island Dogs

"I saw a flash of something," I said, "It wasn't a rat was it?"

"I don't think so. I thought it was a reddish colour."

"Let's have a look in the hole, and find out what it was."

"Okay, I do hope it's not a rat. I don't like them."

Fiona walked behind me as we approached the hole. We peered in, and a small ginger furry face with pointed ears looked back at us.

"Simon, it's a kitten."

Fiona reached in and tried to pick it up, but it ran along the beach back in the direction of the huts.

"That was weird," I said. "What's a kitten doing here?"

"Maybe it belongs to Kapo?"

A small boat puttered past the sandy point at the end of the island, full of ladies sheltering from the sun under umbrellas.

"I reckon that's the public transport from Pangai to some other islands beyond here," I said, "it looks odd to see umbrellas drifting past."

The umbrella ferry disappeared behind the trees.

We were alone again. The sea stretched in front of us, the waves breaking further out over the fringing reef. Fiona photographed me in the shallow water as I stood, parting the waves, pretending I was Moses.

She interrupted my reverie. "We'd better go back to camp to cook dinner before it gets dark. There's no electricity here, remember, and we want to see what we're eating."

Hand in hand, we strolled back through the shallow ripples, in a scene with more romance than a Barbara Cartland novel.

≈ ≈ ≈

A smoky smell wafted along the beach towards us. We headed over to where someone had lit a fire under a grate.

"What shall we have for dinner?" I asked.

"There's a saucepan here; let's heat a tin of spaghetti and meatballs."

"Sounds good. I wish we'd brought fresh bread to mop up the sauce."

"I think we'll be hanging out for any fresh food by the end of the week."

The contents of the tin took no time to heat on the fire, and we ate it straight from the saucepan.

Fiona had an idea. "I'll pour water in the pan and boil it, that'll make washing up easier."

"All right, then let's sit on the beach and watch the sun. It'll be setting soon."

It didn't become any cooler as the daylight faded. The breeze and the volume of the palm trees rustling both increased. As the sun disappeared behind the distant volcanoes, a light appeared at the top of Mark's yacht.

"I wonder what he's having for dinner?" said Fiona.

"He's probably eating spaghetti and meatballs out of a saucepan too."

We laughed at this thought.

"I've noticed something different here compared to night-time in Pangai," said Fiona, "no chickens pokking, or dogs barking."

"You're right, and you know what else? No mosquitos."

"Wow, yes, they haven't bitten me at all."

"I can hear some pigs," I said, "I'm sure it's not Kapo's piglets; these sound a lot bigger."

"There must be some living in the jungle behind us."

"I hope they stay out of our way. Some of those pigs are huge and have big tusks."

Fiona grabbed my hand and pointed at the sky. "Look at the stars, they're so clear. It reminds me of growing up on the farm. There's no light pollution here, it's amazing how much we miss, living in western cities."

We sat on the beach for ages, talking, studying the constellations, listening to the sea rippling, listening to the wind murmur in the trees. Behind us Kapo, Sebastian and their guests were eating dinner on an outdoor setting, by the light of a hurricane lamp.

"Now what?" asked Fiona.

"Bed I reckon, the sun through the tent will wake us very early."

"It's only 8 p.m."

"I know, but think of hopping out of our sheets at dawn and jumping straight into the sea."

"Let's do that, and then a plastic bottle shower."

We opened the tent, climbed in and lay on top of our sleeping bags. With the absence of pokking, the breeze on our faces, and the accompaniment of the waves and murmuring palm trees we had no problem falling asleep.

≈ ≈ ≈

The face of a snuffling piglet appeared in the pre-dawn through the mosquito mesh, its dark nose covered in sand like it had been dunked in brown sugar.

"Good morning piggie," said Fiona, "I think I prefer being woken up by you than by chickens pokking."

"What's the time?" I asked, "I slept so well, I feel great."

Fiona found her watch. "It's 5.15."

"Woh. That's a bit earlier than we usually wake up. The sun hasn't risen yet."

"It's getting light. Race you into the sea."

We pulled swimmers out of our bags, tugged them on and unzipped the tent.

I stood up and stretched, delicious warm pre-sunrise air on my skin. Mirror-flat translucent sea led away to the horizon. The white sand unfolded in both directions. I could just make out the distant volcanoes through the early morning haze. No-one else was awake except the piglets.

"I can't believe we're here." said Fiona, "Our own desert island. Quick, pinch me to wake me up."

"Can I hug you instead?"

Fiona had a white bikini on. Her skin felt warm and soft against mine.

"Come on." She pulled my hand, and we waded into the sea. Our ripples disrupted its surface.

"What's that fish?" I asked. "The one near your leg."

Fiona shrank back against me, then recovered and peered through the water.

"It's the same colour as the sand," she said, "but with a yellow line along it. It's well camouflaged. There's another one. And another. Hundreds."

"They're quite big."

"They are. Err, are there sharks here?" Fiona looked around the surface of the sea for fins. I was tempted to sing the *Jaws* theme, then I saw Fiona's face and realised this would be a Very Bad Idea.

"I can't imagine sharks would come in this close," I said, "Sebastian would have told us if it wasn't safe to swim. Let's pull our snorkels out after breakfast and have a closer look at the fish."

Fiona dived under the water and surfaced. "The water's so clear. It gets deep quickly. I'm out of my depth here."

She swam back to me.

"Shall we lie in the shallows?" she said.

We lay down on our backs, our bottom halves in the water. The sun was rising, and with the dawn breeze, little wavelets washed over us.

The umbrella ferry boat from the unseen islands passed by, filled with the Tongan ladies on their way to Pangai.

"I love this place," I said, "I hope we can come back here many times in our lives."

"It's stunning. But it's not even 6 a.m. and we've an entire day to fill in yet."

"Seriously? Would you prefer to be somewhere else?"

Fiona stood and looked around.

"I'll get used to the peace and quiet, I suppose."

≈ ≈ ≈

"Shall we have breakfast?" I asked. "What have we brought to eat?"

"Cornflakes. Although we don't have any milk. It'll have to be cereal with water."

"Oh. Okay. Nice. Anything else?"

"There's some fresh fruit we'd better eat today before it goes off. This is going to be challenging without a fridge. We take electricity for granted, don't we?"

"Let's keep the fruit for lunch. It should be okay if we put it in the shade."

We sat under palm trees eating our cornflakes and water, then rinsed the bowls. The two dogs dozed under a tree nearby, their lips wuffling at the occasional insect.

"Now what?" I asked.

"I'm going to lie here and read." Fiona retrieved her book from the tent and climbed into the hammock. One of the dogs stood up, stretched its front paws out and then tried to join her.

"No, you won't fit in here with me." She swung in the hammock gently for a while. I sat on the sand and daydreamed. The other dog put its head in my lap, and I patted it absent-mindedly.

"Good morning," said Sebastian, appearing clad in the same denim shorts he'd been wearing yesterday. I wondered if he ever took them off.

"This one's name is Smokey," he said, "and the smaller dog's name is Puppy. Kapo also has a ginger cat around here somewhere, called Rascal."

Fiona and I looked at each other. That explained the kitten we'd seen last night.

"Morning Sebastian," said Fiona. "This place is so relaxing. Do you live here all the time?"

Sebastian sat down on the sand and joined us. "Kapo owns this land. I'm his partner, and I own a share of it. I bought it from a chap called Nils last year. He helped Kapo set up the accommodation."

"We met him," I said, "in Nuku'alofa. Kiwi guy."

"That's him. Anyway, most of the year I work as a lighting technician in the film industry, on location all over the world, I don't have a permanent home. I come here in between shoots. Last month I was working on the second *Jurassic Park* movie in California."

"Wow, that's impressive."

"Filming is intense. Twelve-hour days, seven days a week, dealing with demanding actors and directors who can't agree with each other. This is my retreat away from work. No-one can reach me here. Once a week, Kapo takes me into Pangai and I pick up any messages from the post office. That's how I find out about what I'm working on next. Otherwise, I'm cut off from civilisation. It's great!"

"But what do you find to do while you're here?" Fiona asked.

"Oh, there's plenty to do," said Sebastian. "We're all going snorkelling on the outer reef this morning. Would you like to come with us?" He pointed out to sea, where white-crested waves broke like paint slopping from a tin.

"How are you getting there?" I asked. "It's a long way to swim."

"Mark's going to bring his dinghy over and give us a ride."

I turned to Fiona. "Do you want to do that?"

"I'm not sure about swimming out there; I think I'd prefer to snorkel here in the shallows."

"All right, I'll stay here with you."

We observed Mark's dinghy leave the side of his yacht and head towards the beach, Mark visible in the stern under his floppy hat.

Johnny and Ingrid appeared and walked down to the water's edge to meet him. Sebastian pushed the dinghy off from the sand, turned it round and hopped in. They motored away towards the reef.

I looked on.

I wish I was going with you.

≈ ≈ ≈

Fiona vacated the hammock so that Smokey could jump in. We grabbed our snorkels and our swimmers which were already dry in the heat of the day.

The yellow striped fish were still there as we entered the water. The beach shelved off steeply and we were soon out of our depth. I headed towards a coral head in deeper water.

"That's far enough out for me," said Fiona.

"You'll see some great stuff round the coral heads."

"Come back and tell me about it."

I swam further out until I was about level with Mark's yacht.

If I keep my eye on the yacht for reference, I won't have a repeat of my scare on Atata island.

The coral head was immense, solid, and just under the surface. It was no wonder Kapo had taken great care to avoid them when guiding his boat, the previous day. Swarms of tiny sun-reflecting fish flittered on top of it and around the sides, as if someone had run a roll of kitchen foil through an office shredder.

I sucked air deep into my lungs and dived below the water. I bet myself I could circumnavigate the coral head in one breath.

Bursting for air, I surfaced. Fiona splashed around in the shallows, but in the other direction something was wrong.

Three people stood in the water, a long way out to sea, among the waves breaking on the reef. They waved their arms like malfunctioning windmills. I could also see Mark's dinghy, but no-one was in it. It was drifting by itself. What had happened?

30.
James Bond

I called to Fiona. "Something's happened to Sebastian and the guys. They might need help. I'm going to swim out there."

"What, all that way? Don't be stupid, they must be over a mile away."

"If I can swim as far as the dinghy, I'll be able to climb in and start it. They must have lost it."

"All right, don't do anything dangerous."

The little red boat was still drifting in my direction. With my snorkel on, I floated well, face down. I swam off course constantly and had to look up towards the dinghy and correct my direction. At one point I turned over on my back and rested before continuing.

After about five million strokes of front crawl, I reached the dinghy which was empty. I pulled myself up on the side and fell into it.

"What the hell's that? Gees, you gave me a fright," said a Canadian voice.

I looked down over the far side into the water to find Mark, his floppy hat still on his head, swimming and pushing the dinghy.

"Sorry to scare you Mark, I saw the dinghy drifting by itself and I thought I'd better rescue it. What happened?"

"The outboard motor's broken, I left the others on the reef and I'm pushing it back. They're waving their arms to attract Kapo's attention."

"You must be exhausted. I'll help you push and then I'll find him."

With the two of us propelling the dinghy along we reached the yacht.

"Thanks for your help," said Mark as he tied up. "If you can swim to shore and ask Kapo to pick the others up in his boat, you can all come to the yacht for lunch. Bring your young lady."

"All right, back soon."

I did something I'd only ever seen in the movies. I stood up on the edge of his yacht, held my snorkel in my hand, and dived over the side into the clear turquoise sea. At that instant, I was James Bond.

≈ ≈ ≈

Fiona was sunbathing on her towel as I emerged from the sea.

"Well, hello there Mish Moneypenny," I said, pretending to be Sean Connery, "errr, do you know where Kapo is?"

"Last seen asleep in the hammock, what happened to you?"

I explained how the dinghy had broken down, and Mark had stranded the others on the reef.

We woke Kapo, and the three of us waded out to his boat.

"I'll drop you off on the yacht while I fetch the others," he said, starting the engine. "Can you watch over the side for coral heads?"

We chugged towards the yacht slowly. I knelt in the bow, looking over the front for the dangerous coral capable of ripping the bottom out of a boat. We navigated the passage safely, and Kapo left us on the stern of the yacht. He set off for the rescue on the outer reef, picking up speed. The three figures had stopped waving.

Fiona stepped down into the cockpit. "Wow, I've never been on a proper ocean-going yacht before. This is fantastic."

"She's a great boat," said Mark, "although I'm sorry, I wasn't expecting guests today, and she needs a clean."

"I think she's lovely," said Fiona. "Are we able to have a look inside?"

Mark showed us the cabin and the small galley. "There are three berths down there; I just need some crew to fill them up. I don't suppose you two fancy helping me take her to Auckland, do you?"

"We'd love to," I said, "in fact New Zealand's our next stop. But neither of us have much sailing experience. I haven't sailed since I was a Sea Scout, and that was in a tiny Mirror dinghy."

"I don't have any sailing experience at all," said Fiona. "Sorry Mark, we won't be able to help."

Mark looked disappointed. "I don't want to be giving sailing lessons in the roaring forties. I'll have to wait and hope someone else comes along."

We could hear Kapo's engine approaching and climbed the ladder to help him tie up alongside.

Despite his small galley, Mark produced snacks and drinks for all of us.

"This is generous of you," said Sebastian.

"It has to be eaten; I need to restock with fresh supplies before this lot goes off."

We passed the afternoon lying in the sun on the yacht, diving Bond-like over the side, and messing around in the water. Ingrid lay on the cabin roof in a bikini which just about covered the legal minimum. I reckoned that was her regular sunbathing spot. Johnny and I had an underwater swimming competition, which he won easily by circumnavigating the yacht without surfacing. Fiona blew up a small inflatable, and floated around on her tummy like a human jellyfish.

We climbed up a rope ladder back on deck, and Mark offered us a beer. He and Johnny related exciting tales of their adventures sailing from Canada.

"Still think there's nothing to do here?" asked Sebastian.

I never want to leave.

≈ ≈ ≈

The sun dipped lower in the sky. We thanked Mark for his hospitality and returned to the island on Kapo's boat.

I dropped the anchor myself and hopped over the side into the shallows, then lifted Fiona down, still in her swimmers. I was attuning to this island life.

"Would you like to come fishing tonight?" asked Kapo, "I'm taking the boat to my secret spot I know a few miles out to sea. We can catch some fresh dinner."

The incriminating eye of the fish at the guest house came to mind.

"What do you think, Fiona?"

"I've had a great day, but I want to stay on dry land now. Thanks anyway, Kapo."

"What's for our meal tonight?" I asked, as the others headed up to the huts to prepare for their fishing expedition.

"Instant noodle and crackers. How does that sound?"

"The Michelin guide reports the cuisine at this island restaurant is horrible, with an excellent choice of processed rubbish."

Fiona laughed.

While we heated water for instant noodles, Kapo's boat was loaded with fishing gear, and as the sun reached the horizon, he started the engine and the four anglers headed out to sea.

Fiona and I were alone on the island.

"Let's sit on the beach and watch the stars again," I said.

"Okay, but it's overcast now. I'm not sure how many there'll be tonight."

We ate noodles and crackers, and watched the last of the sun in a thin gap of sky between the edge of the cloud and the sea. The dogs were lying near the hammocks, and the piglets had gone to sleep.

We were the only humans on the island.

We sat close to each other on the sand as the night grew darker.

The clouds hid the stars.

There was no moon.

There were no lights anywhere.

It was pitch black almost immediately.

"The sea's disappeared," said Fiona. "I can still hear it rippling, but I can't even see my feet. I've never been in total blackness before. I don't like it."

She held my hand.

"What was that?" she said.

I jumped up and looked round. "What?"

"That noise, there it is again. A crash. Like a tree falling over."

"It's not one of the dogs is it?" I asked. Another crash. "No, that's not a dog."

"I'm scared, Simon."

I sat back down with Fiona and we huddled together on the sand.

"It must be the wild pigs in the jungle," I said. "We heard them last night. Tonight, they sound.... bigger."

"Shall we climb in the tent?"

"The tent won't protect us from a giant boar. I'm sure the dogs will chase them off," I reassured her. I was fairly sure they wouldn't.

"Just think," said Fiona, quietly. "We're all alone on this island, with no electricity, no daylight for the best part of twelve hours, and with Kapo gone, no way of escaping. It's unnerving."

I can't let her know I'm frightened too. I want to protect her, but I'm helpless.

Neither of us was used to being this remote, this cut off from civilisation and without modern conveniences.

The light on Mark's mast illuminated.

"Hurrah, we're saved." I shouted.

I started talking pirate. "Oi see a ship! A ship I say, Marrster Mate. Four years we've been marooned on this desert island and that's the first sign of life."

Fiona giggled. "You've such an imagination."

The pig noises moved away, and we returned to the tent to sleep. Knowing Mark was within shouting distance was comforting.

≈ ≈ ≈

The cloud had cleared by the morning and at the usual time of 5.15 the sugar-dipped piglets roused us. Kapo's boat swung at anchor; the fishing expedition must have returned during the night. I wondered how he'd navigated the coral heads in the dark.

After our morning swim, shower and cornflakes-with-water breakfast, we were lying in the hammocks entertaining the piglets when Kapo walked past, carrying a petrol can.

"Morning Kapo," I said, "everything all right?"

"The boat won't go. I used all the fuel last night fishing. We had to paddle back. Lucky there was four of us."

"Did you catch anything?"

"Not really. A few small ones."

He laughed and, putting down the petrol can, he demonstrated the size of the catch in the angler's traditional way.

"Where will you buy fuel?" asked Fiona.

"I'll catch a ride into Pangai."

Who's going to take him?

He traipsed some distance along the beach and sat down on the sand, looking out to sea.

We watched him sit for a while.

After about fifteen minutes the little ferry puttered past, full of passengers, umbrellas over their heads as usual. Kapo waved to the boat with his entire arm and it slowed down and headed in towards him. He waded into the shallows and as the boat neared the beach, he passed the empty petrol can to the driver and jumped in after it. The umbrella-wielding Tongan ladies bum-shuffled up to make room for him and the boat reversed back out to sea.

"It's like waiting for the 94 bus in Shepherd's Bush," said Fiona. "I reckon that isn't the first time he's run out of fuel."

"What shall we do today?" I asked.

"Let's take a picnic and walk all the way around the island. We haven't been to the other side yet. We can check out whether there's good snorkelling round there."

"I like that idea. We'd better take hats and sunscreen as well, if we're going to be out all day."

We packed some crackers and plenty of water. It wasn't much of a meal, but we found we didn't feel hungry in the heat.

≈ ≈ ≈

The deserted beach stretched away in front of us, shimmering sand ending in a golden promontory, lapped on both sides by inch deep transparent water. We walked barefoot, picking up shells, holding hands, talking. We rounded the point and discovered a narrow causeway, uncovered at the lowest tides, connected our island with Lifuka island.

"Simon, look," said Fiona, as we came to the part of the beach where the causeway ended, "footprints."

"That's strange, no-one lives up here. Kapo's place is the only building on the island."

The footprints led across the beach and into the jungle. Several people had walked past recently.

We left the causeway behind and continued round the island. The reef was closer to shore here, and the waves broke over it. We found a spot where calm, shallow water formed a natural pool.

"Shall we go for a swim?" I asked.

Fiona looked uncertain.

"If we stay close to the beach," I said, "we'll be safe."

We took off our T-shirts and entered the water. We swam in the shallows, staying far away from the breaking waves on the reef. Fiona looked up.

"Simon, someone's watching us. In the trees. Don't look. Oh, there's two of them. Two men."

31.
An Undiscovered Tribe

I looked, despite her warning. The men walked out of the trees, carrying huge sacks over their shoulders. They lay the sacks down on the beach, smiled and waved at us. We returned the wave, unsure of what to do.

Fiona waded closer to me. "They seem friendly."

"They do, although they've got massive machetes hanging from their belts."

I had this brief image in my mind of a newspaper headline: *Young couple found butchered in shallow grave on remote beach. Discarded Samurai sword found nearby.*

"We can't stay in the sea for ever," I said, "let's put our clothes on and keep walking."

We splashed on to the beach and wrapped our towels around us.

One of the men called out, "Malo 'e leilei."

"Malo 'e leilei," I replied. I approached the men cautiously. "What are you doing here?"

They didn't answer, but one of them opened his bag and showed me the inside, packed with round green coconuts. He lifted his machete, and I took an involuntary step backwards. With a sudden movement he sliced the top off a nut and offered it to me. He made a drinking motion.

The warm liquid inside trickled into my mouth and I was careful not to spill any. I had never had coconut milk straight from the nut before. It tasted different to the tinned milk from Sainsbury's. The man sliced another one and held it out to Fiona.

"Try some," I said, "it's really refreshing."

I guessed they didn't speak any English.

"Fiona, do we have the guidebook with us?" I remembered it had a small section of common phrases.

She pulled it out of our bag and handed it to me.

I flicked through to the back pages, ran my finger down the list of words and said to the man, "*Malo.*" (Thank you.)

"*'Io malo*," he replied. This was on the next line in the phrase book, and I read that it meant, 'you're welcome'.

We smiled at each other. Two more men came out of the jungle, dragging another two heavy sacks.

I became more adventurous with the guidebook.

"*Ko.. hoko.. hingoa.. ko Simon.*" (My name is Simon.)

I'm David Attenborough communicating with an undiscovered rainforest tribe. This is the first time anyone has contacted them. News broadcasters worldwide will pay immense sums of money for my report.

I couldn't find the translation for 'this is Fiona'; I pointed to her and said, "Fiona."

The man who'd given us the coconuts mimicked my action and indicated himself first, then the other three men.

"*Tominiko. Vaitafe. Kelemete. Viliami.*"

"Malo 'e leilei," I said again, exhausting my Tongan language.

We all smiled at each other, awkwardly. I took another sip of coconut.

"We should let them return to their work," said Fiona.

I referred to the guide and, smiling, I said "*Alu'a.*" (Goodbye)

"Alu'a," they all responded.

I held up the coconut, and said again "Malo."

They waved and smiled. We picked up our bags and walked away along the beach.

"It must have been their footprints by the causeway," I said to Fiona. "They were copra farmers. I've read about that industry; they harvest coconuts for the flesh inside. What an experience. I could have spent ages with them."

"I think we were running out of words to say; there's only so many times you can say *hello* and *thank you.* This coconut milk is delicious isn't it, so fresh. And it's filling too, I don't think I need the crackers for lunch."

We finished the milk and threw the empty coconut shells into the trees.

We reached the other end of the island.

"This is where we were yesterday," I said. "After we'd seen the cat. We've walked round the entire island. Those hills in the distance must be where those little boats full of Tongans come from."

We strolled in the afternoon heat. A dredger chugged past offshore. One of the little umbrella ferries crossed its path. Shells containing hermit crabs ran around on the beach in all directions. Other larger crabs waved their claws and scuttled away as we approached. Life here hadn't altered since these crustaceans' distant ancestors had witnessed the *Bounty* mutiny.

"I can see Kapo's place ahead," I said.

"Good. I need to lie down in a hammock," said Fiona, "it's too hot to be out."

≈ ≈ ≈

Kapo's boat wasn't at its anchorage; he must have filled it with the petrol and motored somewhere. The dogs were unconscious beneath the trees, and the piglets had deflated on the sand like small bean bags. We reached the hammocks and collapsed into them. An afternoon nap came easily.

The sound of Fiona rummaging in the tent throwing possessions out of bags woke me. I fell out of the hammock and went to investigate.

"What are you doing?"

"We've run out of food. I don't know how we miscalculated, but we've nothing for dinner tonight. Or for tomorrow."

"Mmmm that's going to be a problem. We could ask Kapo and Sebastian if they've any spare."

"They're not here. No-one's here."

"What about Mark? He said he had food on the yacht he needed to use, as it was past its best date. I'll swim out and buy some from him. Do you want to swim with me?"

"I'll stay here; it's a bit far."

I stripped off my shorts and jumped into the sea. It was a few minutes swim to the yacht. I climbed up the rope ladder.

"Anyone home?" I was sure Mark would be there, but I didn't want to surprise him.

"Come on in."

The warmth of the late afternoon sun dried my skin instantly.

"Mark, you mentioned you had some food that needed eating. We've run out, and we were wondering whether we could buy any from you?"

"Sure, you can have some; I'm throwing it out anyway. No need to pay me. Here, how much do you need?"

"Just dinner for two nights. A couple of tins will do."

"Have four, just in case. Here's some tinned meat, spaghetti, and tinned fruit. They're a bit past their sell-by dates, but they'll be fine. I'll give you a carrier bag, and you can swim them back with you."

"Thanks Mark, you're a lifesaver."

I climbed down the rope ladder with the four tins in the bag, and swam with one hand while dragging it clumsily through the water with the other. This was like the particularly sadistic Duke of Edinburgh endurance tests my school referred to as 'character building'. I collapsed face down on the sand, and threw the bag in Fiona's direction.

"Your grocery delivery, Madam."

Fiona looked inside. "It's going to be pot luck tonight, the labels have washed off."

≈ ≈ ≈

After an unconventional dinner of spaghetti and peaches we sat on the beach and chatted. The sun had begun to set when Kapo's boat appeared and dropped anchor offshore. Sebastian and Kapo hopped out, followed by a slight young man who carried a backpack. He had tanned skin and long blonde hair, another Pacific Island sun worshipper.

"Hey guys," said Sebastian, as they walked up the beach, "come and meet Rupert."

"Hi Rupert," I said, "welcome to paradise."

I turned to Sebastian. "Have Johnny and Ingrid gone?"

"Yes, we took them back to Pangai and found Rupert waiting for us."

Rupert dropped his backpack on the sand and gazed at the sparse facilities.

"This place is fantastic. The sea looks so inviting. I can't wait for the morning."

"I'll show you to your room," Sebastian said to Rupert.

"See you guys tomorrow," said Rupert, "nice to meet you."

The three of them walked up to the accommodation, turned the hurricane lamp on and began to prepare an evening meal.

"At least we're not marooned alone on a desert island again," said Fiona.

≈ ≈ ≈

The following morning, Fiona and I jumped in the shallows for our usual swim. We snorkelled up and down the beach in lines like we were mowing the sea. As we dried off on the sand and played with the piglets, Rupert walked over.

"Morning guys," he said, "I saw you snorkelling and wondered if I could come with you?"

"Sure, of course," I replied.

"I'm writing a marine biology thesis," he said, "making my way round the Pacific, recording the different species of fish, and comparing the variety of sea life in different countries. What have you seen here?"

"Well, I don't know all their names, but there's lots of colourful fish around the coral heads. There's a big brain coral this side of the yacht. Do you want to swim to it?"

"I'll stay on the beach," said Fiona, "I don't feel safe all the way out there."

Rupert and I waded into the water and swam to the coral head, enveloped in fish darting into crannies. We dived and circled it, then surfaced, out of breath.

Rupert raved about the underwater pageant. "This is fantastic, Simon, the life is incredible here. Wrasses, parrotfish, angelfish, sweetlips, bannerfish. I think there was a leopard ray in the distance."

I'm snorkelling with Jacques Cousteau. Rupert really knows his fish.

We swam over the top of the coral head; we could have stretched out and touched it. Rupert peered into the crevices, studying his sea life.

A voice shouted from above.

"Hey Simon, want to come up for a coffee? I've just made one."

"Let's go over to the yacht," I said to Rupert, "I'll introduce you to Mark."

We climbed up the rope ladder, and Mark and Rupert shook hands.

Mark handed us steaming mugs.

"One thing I insisted on when I kitted out this yacht was a good coffee machine," he said.

Despite the hot weather, warm coffee that morning was welcome.

"What brings you to Tonga, Rupert?" Mark asked.

Rupert explained about his marine biology studies.

"Which islands have you been to?"

"I've studied the underwater world in Hawaii, Fiji and Samoa, and now Tonga. Only one more island group needed, and I'll have all the material to complete my thesis."

I could see Mark had an idea forming.

"Rupert, can you sail?"

"I can. My father has a yacht in Marina del Rey, in California. I've been crewing for him since I was a boy. Day sailing though, I've never done an overnighter."

"How would you like to study the fish in the Kermadecs?"

"The Kermadecs? I've never heard of them. Where are they?"

"The Kermadec Islands are a marine reserve, halfway between here and New Zealand. They're uninhabited apart from a few scientists and they're impossible to travel to unless you've your own yacht."

"Wow, that'd be a dream. A section about the marine life in another group of islands would finish off my thesis nicely. Are you headed there?"

Mark edged forward in his seat, heading for the climax of his proposal.

"Rupert, would you be my crew to Auckland? We could stop in the Kermadecs for a few days, unless the weather is too rough. How does that sound?"

"Wow, amazing, thanks for the offer. Yes, I would, very much. When are you thinking of leaving? I want to spend at least another week in Tonga if that's okay."

"No problem, I have to resupply, and the dinghy's motor needs a part, which I hope I can buy in Nuku'alofa. Do we have a deal?"

They stood up and shook hands.

"Celebrations all round." Mark produced a bottle of rum and poured three small glasses. We clinked them and drank.

"I'll catch up with you later, skipper." said Rupert.

I shook Mark's hand. "It's been great to meet you Mark. Fiona and I leave tomorrow; we probably won't see you again. I just want to say; I'll never forget the experience of diving from the side of your yacht into the tropical sea. In fact, I'm going to do it again."

Rupert and I stood on the side, masks in our hands, and executed perfect synchronised splashes into the water. We snorkelled back past the coral head to the beach.

"Where did you get to?" asked Fiona, "I thought you'd drowned; I couldn't see you."

"Err, we've been having a rum on Mark's yacht."

"Simon, it's not even nine o'clock in the morning."

"We had a bit of a celebration. I'll tell you about it."

We spent the rest of the day relaxing, swimming and sunbathing.

I knew I was going to miss this place very much indeed.

≈ ≈ ≈

We dismantled the tent without talking the following morning, sad that we were leaving paradise. We swam and bottle-showered for the final time, patted the dogs and the piglets, said goodbye to Sebastian and Rupert and waded out to Kapo's boat. The engine started, and I had a last glance over my shoulder, before resuming my important position in the bow watching for the coral heads.

Kapo tied up at the wharf in Pangai. It felt like we'd been away for weeks.

I shook Kapo's hand and watched his boat as it headed back out to sea.

"Now what?" asked Fiona.

"Now? Now, we have a royal appointment."

Two miles of walking lay ahead of us between the boat dock and our accommodation, free breakfast, and half price dinner at the Lifuka Beach Hotel. We shouldered our packs and walked deliberately, step by step, the dust covering our sandals. The straps of the backpacks rubbed our sweaty skin, and we rested as soon as we found some shade on the outskirts of Pangai town.

A triumphal arch was being constructed across the road, Tongan style.

"That wasn't there before," said Fiona, "I wonder what it's for?"

We sat down on our packs and watched the work.

Four upright palm tree trunks leant in, two on either side of the road, and high above them a horizontal trunk formed an arch. Large palm fronds and coloured lights decorated it. Men stood precariously on rickety twig-constructed wooden ladders, poking the leaves into position, and tidying it up.

"Something's coming," said Fiona, pointing through the arch.

A four-wheel-drive vehicle rushed towards us along the airport road, a blue flashing light on its roof announcing its importance, its siren breaking the peace, an alien noise in the rural scene.

The men building the arch jumped down, picked up their ladders and hid in the trees at the side of the road.

"What's going on?" I asked, "why are the men hiding from the police?"

32.
Drunk and Dishorderly

The blue flashing light passed under the arch; the word *Police* written in white on the doors. A second blue vehicle followed it, with the licence plate HM 1, and a rusty khaki pickup truck formed the rear of the motley procession.

Some pedestrians bowed their heads at the car as it whizzed by.

"That must have been the king and queen," I said, gazing after the convoy as it executed a sudden left turn and disappeared.

We picked up our backpacks and walked under the arch. On the other side, a handwritten sign stated *Welcome Your Majesty* above hand-drawn pictures of assorted well-fed livestock.

"Those men finished the arch ten seconds before the royal cavalcade drove under it," said Fiona, as the workers climbed back out from their hiding place in the trees and brushed themselves off.

I wasn't listening.

I've been within metres of the King of Tonga. And hopefully the queen.

≈ ≈ ≈

The manager of the Lifuka Beach Hotel stood behind the reception desk, her mouth in a straight line, glasses shoved up on her head, hair in disarray.

"What do you mean, you want free breakfast and half-price dinner? We're not a bloody charity."

"I know, but the Tongan lady I spoke to last week offered us that deal, and we've come here in good faith."

"Which Tongan lady?"

"She was sitting out near the beach in a chair. In fact, she's there right now."

I pointed out of the reception area.

The manager sighed in exasperation.

"I don't know how I'm supposed to make a profit here with free breakfasts and half-price dinners. The owners employed me to make this place work, and they're not helping."

I concluded that the Tongan lady who spent her life immobile in the chair was the owner.

"All right, if she made that offer, I'll have to honour it. Here's the key; furthest cabin away down the beach. I'm Linda. Shout out if you need anything. Dinner's at six."

There wasn't much to explore at the hotel, just the reception which doubled as an outdoor dining area, and the little accommodation huts surrounding it. We soon found ourselves back on the beach where the Tongan lady was snoring like a sequence of deflating whoopee cushions.

"Let's see if anyone's at the dive shop," I said.

Next door the same sign said, 'back in ten minutes.'

"Far out," said Fiona, "that's the longest ten minutes in history."

"I hope someone's around tomorrow morning. With the feast in the evening and church with the royals on Sunday it's my last chance to dive here."

"I'm hungry," said Fiona. "Have we got any food with us?"

"Not really. Let's go back to Pangai and find something for lunch."

≈ ≈ ≈

The forthcoming royal visit had pressed the residents of Pangai into atypical activity. Ladies in colourful dresses swept dust from the streets, palm tree fronds decorated shops, and The Royal Bank of Tonga had even erected new advertising material, in the event the king suddenly required a personal loan.

At my insistence, we went into the local Royal Tongan Airlines office and reconfirmed the plane from Vava'u was stopping in Ha'apai to pick us up.

We'd changed travellers' cheques, eaten some bread and cheese for lunch, and bought postcards and stamps when Fiona found a fruit stall.

"Look at the size of those watermelons," she said. "Are they the same ones we get in Sainsbury's?"

"They're the same colour, just larger."

Fiona approached the stall and placed her hand on a melon.

"Do you sell slices of melon?" she asked the shopkeeper.

"No, just whole."

"How are we going to carry it, Simon?"

"Find the smallest one you can, I reckon." We were going to be having plenty of rest stops on the way home.

Fiona picked out a melon slightly larger than a basketball and we took it in turns to carry it.

The Tongan lady was still sleeping in her chair when we returned. We observed her from some distance away.

"Does she ever move?" asked Fiona, quietly, "I feel like poking her to find out."

I laughed, and the lady woke up and looked around. She stared at us without recognition and returned to her usual level of consciousness.

"I think we should join her," said Fiona, trying not to giggle.

The warm breeze wafted over us as we sat on two loungers we'd pushed together. We cut a chunk out of the watermelon with my penknife, an implement completely unsuited to this task, and ate it, dribbling juice on to the sand.

Fiona reached for my hand.

"Lying on a beach, eating tropical fruits, what else do we need to make our holiday complete?" she said.

"I really hope we can see the queen this weekend. Then I'll have ticked off everything I came to Tonga for."

"Well, we know the king is here; the sign on the arch said so."

We lay down and snuggled together.

Linda's voice came from the reception area, in the style of Sybil from *Fawlty Towers*.

"Dinner will be served in the hotel dining room in ten minutes."

≈ ≈ ≈

We ate, all sitting round one table and sharing the fish, taro, crabmeat, coleslaw, plantain, beef and vegetables, bread, and melon. Linda sat with us, as did the two other guests in the hotel, Peter, an Australian engineer of about 50 years old who was in Tonga for a few days fixing an industrial pump, and Kurt, who was drunk.

Kurt was also aged around 50. His skin was considerably older than him. He had red hair, and a very red face with tiny veins covering his cheeks. His bulbous, pitted nose advertised his successful drinking career. He shook my hand vigorously and introduced himself.

"Pleeeshterrmeetyerr. I'm Kurt."

I thought he might be English; it was hard to tell.

Conversation commenced in the usual awkward way, when people who have never met are forced together.

"I flew in today," said Peter, "and I've had many experiences in my life, but that's the only time I can say I've flown with a king."

"Wow, something to tell the grandkids." I said, adding, "was the queen with him by any chance?"

"He had a bit of an entourage; one of the ladies might have been the queen. I'm sorry, I don't know what she looks like."

She might be here. There's hope for an encounter.

"I," announced Kurt, thumping the table so hard his empty beer glass fell into his lap, "I've shpent sh… shome… some time with the King of Thailand."

He looked at us to ensure he had our attention. I couldn't resist encouraging him.

"Go on Kurt, give us the details."

"Well, I haven't exactly shpent time with the King of Thailand. But I did shpend a night in a Bangkok prison At His Majeshhty's Pleasure. Hurrr Hurrr Hurrr Hurrr!"

He laughed raucously at his own joke.

"And what, Kurt, were you in prison for in Bangkok?" I asked.

"Drunk and Dishorderly, of coursh. Hurr Hurr Hurr."

Linda rolled her eyes. I wondered how many nights she had endured his presence at the dining table.

Kurt continued, mournfully.

"I've brought shome tins of corned beef with me."

We digested this piece of information.

"Why, Kurt, have you brought tins of corned beef?" asked Peter.

"It shaid in the tourisht information, you musht bring corned beef, for the poor people here who have no food. I've an entire shootcashe of corned beef."

"Well, that's very kind of you," I said, meaning it, and seeing Kurt in a new light. Despite his obvious addiction, he must have a generous heart.

"Unfortunately," continued Kurt, "I've losht the shootcashe."

"Ah. Where did you last see it?" I asked.

"At the airport. I forgot about it. Sh'gone."

It wasn't clear which airport he meant, but I hoped it was one in Tonga and some of the 'poor people' had benefited from it.

As the evening drew on, we excused ourselves and headed for bed. Peter left too, and Kurt had already passed out. Linda whispered he did this every evening and then made a lot of noise during the night crashing around reception trying to find the toilet. I could tell she felt sorry for him though. They were around the same age, and I reckoned they were both lonely.

As we lay down under our mosquito net, Fiona noticed something.

"No dogs or chickens," she said, "It's peaceful, same as Kapo's island."

"I suppose it's because we're a little way outside the town. I love the sound of the waves breaking on the beach."

≈ ≈ ≈

Neither Kurt nor Linda were present for breakfast. Peter was finishing his food as we arrived and soon left to begin work on his pump.

After breakfast, I grabbed my dive gear and headed next door to the dive store. Fiona wanted to relax and read her book.

A note saying *open* superseded the *back in ten minutes* sign, and I knocked. A tall, muscly, tattooed man opened the door.

"Guten Morgen (good morning)," he said, "do you want to come diving?"

"Yes please, I've got my own gear with me."

"Good. We are just leaving. You can come with us. I'm Kristof, this is my old schoolfriend Henrik, he's visiting me from Germany."

I introduced myself, and at his instruction, lifted my gear into his long thin open boat which was sitting on a trailer behind an old pickup truck. Kristof threw in an extra two tanks of air and a weight belt.

"Hang on, I will reverse the boat into the water."

He hopped into the pickup, pausing to turn the *open* sign round, so it once again read *back in ten minutes*.

Tanned and shirtless standing at the centre cockpit of his boat, bleached blond hair flying behind him, Kristof had perfected the image of a Pacific island playboy. Henrik sat in the bow under a hat, a much slighter young chap with a closely cropped dark beard.

The journey towards Kao and Tofua volcanoes lasted around 30 minutes. We conversed on the way over the noise of the powerful engine.

"Simon, have you done much diving?"

"I've done around 60 dives including some in Tongatapu."

"Oh wow, you will have seen a lot."

Which part of Germany are you from, Kristof?"

"The part that used to be East Germany. I was in the army, and when unification happened, my service ended, and I headed off travelling. I have been here only a few months myself, but not sure how long I will stay, it's a bit remote."

Henrik was in Tonga for a couple of weeks holiday. He wasn't diving, but he had a banana-coloured surfboard with him. I wondered what he was going to do with it.

We arrived at our first dive site and kitted up.

"This is Aquarium Reef," announced Kristof.

Henrik set up a fishing rod, as Kristof and I disappeared under the surface.

Thousands of multi-coloured small fish populated Aquarium Reef. I needed Rupert with me; fish identification wasn't my area of expertise. I realised diving this spot was a privilege few humans would have ever experienced.

We climbed back on the boat.

"Now," said Kristof, "we will go to an uninhabited island."

This was exciting news. We motored back the way we'd come and beached the boat on the smallest piece of land I had ever seen. Sand fringed a miniscule clump of a dozen trees, in a perfect children's picture book interpretation of a desert island.

"What's this island called, Kristof?"

"Nukupule. We will stop here for lunch."

Kristof and Henrik pulled out a small barbecue and cooked some fish Henrik had caught during our dive. I took my bag of crackers, a slice of our huge watermelon, and some fruit pinched from breakfast and wandered round to the other side of the island. This took two minutes.

I sat on the sand.

I looked out to sea.

No ships.

I was Robinson Crusoe.

Marooned on this tiny island following a shipwreck, the only survivor, I had swum, exhausted, holding on to a plank of wood, through rough seas until I washed up here. My beard has grown three feet long. I've lived on nothing but coconuts and coconut milk. I haven't seen another human for years. I've forgotten what humans look like.

"Hey Simon, where are you, do you want a beer?"

Kristof's shout through the trees punctured my imagination.

"Sure, thanks, I'll come round."

We sat and drank beer on the beach.

"I was imagining what it'd be like to be marooned on this island, with no food, no water, nothing."

"Would you like to find out? I can leave you here." Kristof laughed.

"No thanks, that'd be a bit too real."

"I tell you what, I can show you what to do if you ever are stranded on an island like this. Come with me."

He led me into the trees.

"When I said I was in the East German army, I was actually in the commandos. We were taught how to survive in the jungle with nothing at all."

He picked up a large green coconut and handed it to me.

"Here, you open this."

I knew that to reveal the milk and flesh inside the coconut, I had to remove the thick outer green husk, and uncover the brown nut, which itself would need cracking.

I held the nut above my head and flung it on the ground as hard as I could. It was undamaged. I threw it down on top of another green coconut. I bashed the two coconuts together. They both remained undented.

"I give up. I need a machete."

"You have no machete; you are shipwrecked on the island with nothing. Here, I will teach you how to have the choice between life and death."

This is exciting. I'm going to learn jungle survival from a master.

Kristof found a small young palm tree about a metre high. He pulled all the leaves off it, and it became a stick. He found a broken coconut shell, and using it as a sharp edge, he shaved the tree-stick into a point at its top.

"Watch this."

He took the green coconut and bashed it on the pointed stick a few times. The husks separated from the inner, and he pulled them away with his hands, exposing the brown nut. He pointed at the *eyes* on the coconut, dark spots on its shell. He put the sharp stick against these eyes and twisted down. I heard a slight cracking noise.

"We have to be careful, we don't want to lose the milk."

He pushed down a bit more on the coconut and pulled it off the stick quickly. He inverted it and handed it to me. A thin crack showed in the top of it, like broken crockery that Araldite has failed to fix properly.

"You should be able to drink from that."

I tried. It wasn't as neat as the machete chop the man on Kapo's island had done, and the milk ran down my front, but I could make some enter my mouth.

"And that is how you survive when you have no tools."

"Thank you, I hope I never need that skill, but it's good to know."

"Come on, let's go diving."

Mushroom Reef was different to Aquarium reef. We swam down the anchor line deeper and deeper into the unknown. Larger fish drifted by, and once we neared the bottom, we couldn't see the surface above us. I looked at Kristof and he made a sign with the flat of his hand vertical in front of his face. I knew what that meant.

Big Shark.

33.
Kava and The King

Several sharks lay motionless on the bottom, a few metres below us.

I kept a wary eye on them. These were bigger than the reef sharks I had shown Rick and Pamela, and the species was unknown to me. I wasn't sure if they were dangerous.

We couldn't stay underwater long, owing to our depth, so we slowly swam to the surface, our small bubbles rising ahead of us as if we were floating in an immense SodaStream bottle.

"What sort of sharks were they?" I asked Kristof, as we clambered on board.

"Bull sharks."

"Are they dangerous?"

"Yes, they can bite, but they won't unless they're provoked."

I wondered if anyone had confirmed this with the sharks.

I had a question for Henrik.

"Why did you bring your surfboard?"

"I brought it all the way from Germany on the plane, but the wind hasn't been right for surfing. Kristof's going to give me a tow."

He flipped the board in the water and jumped in after it. Kristof produced a rope, and threw one end to Henrik. He tied the other end to a cleat on the boat.

"Ready?"

Henrik held on to the rope, and Kristof gunned the engine. Henrik fell into the water and left the surfboard behind. He shouted at Kristof.

"Can you try again, not so fast this time?"

Henrik swam back to the board and climbed on.

"Ready?"

The boat started off slowly, and the board buried itself and headed for the seabed, taking Henrik with it. They both popped up again.

"A bit faster, and I'll try further back on the board. I might start kneeling down."

Kristof pulled in the rope and threw it to Henrik a third time. The rope became taut, Kristof pulled away slowly and towed Henrik in a kneeling position. He was wobbling dramatically, and it didn't seem easy to steer.

He shouted to us.

"Keep that speed. I'm going to try to stand up."

He was on one knee, then crouching, then standing up.

"Don't change speed. Keep going straight," he shouted.

The boat headed towards the beach.

Henrik was still standing up. He let go with one hand, punched the air several times in celebration, and fell backwards with a spectacular somersault.

"Kristof, stop," I said, "he's fallen in."

Kristof stopped. He turned the boat round.

The board floated by itself.

We couldn't see Henrik.

We drifted slowly, our hands shielding our eyes, searching the surface of the water.

"There." I pointed.

Henrik was a long way behind the board, floating on his back. He raised one hand to indicate he was still alive. The boat approached him.

He lifted his head.

"Owwwww. I think that's enough surfing for today."

We pulled the bruised Henrik and his board on to the boat and sped back to the beach. I collected my dive gear together, thanked Kristof and went to find Fiona.

≈ ≈ ≈

Fiona lay on the bed in a long summer dress I hadn't seen before, her hair tied in a bun.

"Hello," I said, "you're dressed up. What's the occasion?"

"The feast, Simon, or had you forgotten?"

In the excitement of shark diving, learning shipwreck survival techniques, and rescuing injured surfers, I had.

I threw on my well-used Hawaiian shirt, splashed water on my face and we left.

"Fiona, we need to run."

"I can't run in flip-flops. You run. I'll catch you."

"I can't go without you. Hurry up."

"I'm going as fast as I can."

We entered Pangai and speed-walked towards the rugby field.

There wasn't a spare patch of grass under the family groups sitting on picnic rugs and chairs. Palm leaves formed a roof to a pavilion on a small stage. Huge mats lay on long white rows of tables, almost invisible under the plates of food covering them. Small, cooked pigs were speared from mouth to bottom on long poles leaning up at an angle.

I had no idea how we were going to find Tomasi. I needn't have worried; he ran up to us.

"Hello, Simon, Fiona, welcome, welcome."

"Hello Tomasi, I'm so sorry we're late. Wow. This is amazing, I've never seen this much food."

"Our families work together to prepare; everyone has brought something."

Tomasi's family were sitting at one of the long tables. The food buried the palm leaf mat running the length of it. They'd reserved two vacant chairs in the centre for us.

"You're my guests of honour," he explained.

We both felt uncomfortable at the accolade, embarrassed we hadn't brought anything.

"We call a Tongan feast a *kaipola*," said Tomasi. "*Kai* is our word for food, and *pola* refers to the table mat. My mother and grandmother made this one."

Two ladies near the end of the table smiled and waved. The younger of the two still retained a few teeth.

"The food shows love," he said, "the more food, the more love. That's why there is so much."

"Where are the king and queen?" I asked.

"The king came and ate earlier; he wasn't here long. I didn't see the queen."

This was a disaster. Not only had the queen not been here, but we'd also missed seeing the king.

"In Tongan culture, no-one eats before the king eats, and everyone must sit lower down than the king. No-one can stand up before him either. The king will come and eat first, and then he might leave, so everyone else can relax and enjoy the food."

"You don't think he ate too much and had to have a lie down?"

"Simon, you can't say that." He looked around to make sure no-one had heard me. "You can't say anything bad about the king."

Oh no. I've made a serious social faux pas.

"I hope he'll be at church tomorrow," I said, trying to redeem myself.

"I'm sure he will. The band has been practising so hard. Anyway, eat, please."

We weren't sure where to start. A whole pig lay in the centre. Fiona and I avoided looking at the head, although the other end had a crispy curly tail which we weren't used to seeing so prominently displayed on our Sunday roast. Sliced beef and lobsters were on other platters, surrounded by fish, taro leaves, yams, and sweet potatoes.

We were unsure how much to take, we didn't want to appear rude by not eating, we were also aware Tonga was a poor country, and the local people would need the food in front of us. We filled our plates with a little of everything, copying Tomasi's other family members, as we pulled pieces of meat off the platters.

While we ate, three different choirs took turns to sing haunting, harmonic local music, accompanied by men playing guitars.

We ate as much as we could.

We had no chance of keeping up with the Tongans.

"Have some more," Tomasi offered us a plate piled with pig.

"I'd love to," said Fiona, "but I'm so full."

"You must take some away with you," he said, "we mustn't waste any. People will take all of this to eat later."

We promised we'd take some food back to our hotel. Maybe Kurt could use it to replace his missing suitcase of corned beef.

Uncle Mafu appeared. "Hello, thank you for coming to our feast; it's an honour to have you with us."

"It's wonderful of you to invite us Mafu, so generous."

"Come, Tomasi, bring our guest and join me and my brothers for kava."

Bring our guest.

Guest singular.

Not 'guests'.

Tomasi stood up and asked me to follow him. He spoke to his mother. "Could you please talk to Fiona, while Simon and I join the kava ceremony?"

He turned to Fiona. "I'm sorry, kava is traditionally something only men do."

"It's okay," said Fiona, "I had a bit at the Tongan National Centre and I'm not fussed about it." She sat down next to the older ladies.

I followed Tomasi and Mafu.

≈ ≈ ≈

I tried not to let my anxiety show. There was a whole ceremony and process around kava, and I knew nothing of it.

What if I accidentally insult them?

What if I mistakenly declare war?

What if they put me in the cooking pot?

Tomasi noticed my concern. "Just follow me, do what I do. Half of these guys don't know what they're doing either."

A wide circle of men sat round a huge wooden bowl on stumpy feet. People shifted round to make room for Tomasi and me. Mafu took his place on the opposite side of the circle. The smoke from a fire burning next to the wooden bowl stung my eyes, before it changed direction and bothered people opposite.

I noted the proceedings carefully. I was aware this was a ceremony few westerners were privileged to witness.

A man in a black shirt and woven mat walked into the centre of the circle and picked up a wooden ladle and a coconut shell. He scooped some kava out of the bowl and poured it into the shell.

Uncle Mafu clapped and took the coconut shell. He drank deeply, then made a sudden motion as if to throw the dregs over his shoulder. He flung the shell back where the server retrieved it.

I made a mental note of the procedure.

The next man repeated the motions, clapping, drinking, and throwing.

I hoped I wouldn't make a mistake.

It was my turn. Everyone was looking at me.

I remembered to clap.

The server handed me the bowl of kava.

I drank all of it. It tasted of the same revolting second-hand dishwater. I hoped no-one had noticed my grimace.

I threw the dregs over my shoulder. The kava dripped on to my Hawaiian shirt.

"Throw the shell," whispered Tomasi.

I flung the shell back at the server. This was an unnatural action, but he picked it up and continued with the next man.

I had passed my Tongan initiation ceremony.

Tomasi put his hand on my shoulder in a gesture of friendship.

The kava bowl passed round the circle multiple times.

The clapping, drinking and throwing procedure continued.

I had no idea if I was supposed to feel drunk or stoned. I felt neither.

I had to stop drinking dishwater. My bladder was about to rupture.

"Tomasi," I whispered, "would I be rude if I left the kava circle? It's getting dark, and Fiona and I should probably go home."

"It's fine," he said, "just leave quietly. I'll see you tomorrow at church."

Two other men also clambered to their feet.

I remembered no-one could leave a feast before the guest of honour, and I hoped the men hadn't been waiting for me.

≈ ≈ ≈

I found Fiona with the ladies, and we made our excuses.

As soon as we were an appropriate distance away from the feast, we both dived into the bushes.

"How do the Tongans hold their bladders so long?" I asked, generously watering a hibiscus bush.

"No idea," said Fiona, noisily peeing behind a small palm tree. "I'm glad we left when we did; I've been busting for ages."

We surreptitiously exited the jungle and walked further up the road.

"That feast was an incredible experience," I said, "especially the kava ceremony, Tomasi fully initiated me into Tongan society. What were you talking about with his mother?"

"God and Jesus, mostly, not my specialised subject. I was happy to nod and smile. She wanted to know all about my parents, and how big their church was. I didn't want to admit they never enter one except for weddings and funerals."

≈ ≈ ≈

The heat of the sun on our faces woke us the next morning.

"It's Sunday, Fiona, we're going to church with the king and queen."

"I hope she turns up. You'll be disappointed if she's not there."

After a hotel breakfast of cornflakes, toast, hard-boiled egg, papaya and pineapple we headed out.

The congregation were mingling outside, and we sat in the same seats as the previous week. A few people smiled at us and waved in recognition. There weren't any other westerners at the service, so we were easy to spot.

Well before ten o'clock, all the people had sat down, but spare seats were visible around the church, and the atmosphere was more subdued.

"There aren't as many people here as last week," I said. "That's odd. I thought everybody would be here to see their majesties."

"I was thinking the same thing. Maybe they all have kava hangovers."

The choir entered, then the musicians. I glimpsed Tomasi carrying his trumpet. Everyone stood up.

A moment's silence followed, then the priest entered from a side door, followed by the extensive form of His Majesty Tupou IV. The king stepped up to a throne next to the band and choir, facing into the centre of the church. I observed his seat was the highest, as dictated by protocol. The door behind him had been closed. No-one else could enter.

"The queen's sitting in the front already, I suppose?" I asked, not very hopefully.

"If she's here."

The priest bowed, spoke a short introduction, and then, copying the congregation, we took our seats. The band leader also bowed to the king, who ignored him. This time, the service started with the silver band playing the Christmas carol medley they'd entertained us with last week. It was Tomasi's big moment.

I restrained myself from singing along, although I couldn't help tapping my foot.

Fiona prodded me.

"Sit still."

"Sorry, it's very catchy."

The king sat, unimpressed with the proceedings.

The service continued in the same vein as the previous week. The priest read each verse of the hymns, then the choir and congregation repeated them. I lost sight of the king while people stood in front of me, and I couldn't see if he was joining in.

As last week, the sermon began in Tongan.

I looked at the floor, arms resting on my legs, hands clasped, listening to the monotone voice.

After five minutes, I popped my head up and caught sight of His Majesty.

Asleep.

Fast asleep.

Out cold.

His head rested on his chest, which rose and fell as he breathed. No-one else was looking in his direction, they were all focussed on the preacher.

"Fiona, the king's gone to sleep."

"I'm not surprised, it won't be long before I join him."

"Yes, but he's in full view of everyone."

"Sssshh, don't forget, no-one's allowed to disrespect or criticise him. If the king wants to sleep, the king sleeps."

And so the priest continued with his sermon, while the king continued with his after-breakfast nap.

The service concluded with a final hymn which roused His Majesty. The Priest spoke some last words and invited the king to leave the church via the side door.

≈ ≈ ≈

"Fiona, if we nip out now, we might catch sight of the royal couple. I must see if the queen is here."

The second the king had left, everybody sat down. We excused ourselves, exited via the rear doors and rounded the side of the building just in time to observe the king climbing into the light blue vehicle HM 1. Other people were already in the car, and several smart looking officials stood guard.

I took a quick photograph of the king's extravagant backside wriggling into the car door, an official standing beside him with an umbrella, shielding the royal personage from the sun.

"Damn," I said, "One of the people in the car might be the queen."

"Let's sprint across the field towards the gate at the edge of the churchyard," said Fiona, "and catch the convoy as it goes past."

I could feel the disapproving eyes of the officials on us as we ran across the field. I didn't care.

If the queen's here, I can't miss her.

We reached the entrance.

We selected a suitable vantage point.

Near enough to see.

Far enough not to be obvious.

The dark blue police four-wheel drive set off from the church, blue light flashing, succeeded by HM 1 and the khaki vehicle. I took a quick picture of the convoy approaching. They were travelling rapidly, and as they passed, I snapped another. Two ladies were visible in HM 1's third row of seats. One of them waved at us. Fiona waved back.

"Fiona, was that the queen?"

34.
A Time to Kill

"I'm not sure if it was the queen in the back of the car," said Fiona. "It was hard to see. She looked very young. It could have been the king's hairdresser for all I know."

"Damn. Damn, Damn," I said, "so close."

"I'm sorry, Simon. It might not have been her. Let's go back to the church and find Tomasi."

≈ ≈ ≈

Tomasi was chatting with other members of his band. They were all dressed in their white and blue band uniform.

"Hey Simon," he said, "did you take a picture of the king?"

"I did, or at least his rear view, but I don't think the queen was with him. I really wanted to see her."

"Sorry Simon. Uncle Mafu told me she wasn't on this trip to Ha'apai at all. Never mind, maybe you'll find her in Nuku'alofa. You're headed back soon?"

I'm never going to see her now.

"We return tomorrow, Tomasi. We've loved the Ha'apai Islands, so friendly and relaxing. And such an unforgettable experience at the feast. Thank you for inviting us."

"My pleasure. Where are you staying tonight?"

"We're at the Lifuka Beach Hotel, about two miles out of town."

"Would you like a ride? We're headed that way. We're playing at a church on Foa island this afternoon."

"I thought people couldn't drive on Sundays?"

"There are a couple of exceptions. I mean, the king can; he can drive when he likes. But we can drive on Sunday if we're going to church, so this will be okay."

"Sounds good. Will there be enough room for us and all of you?"

"No problem."

Tomasi led us over to an old blue pickup truck. Uncle Mafu was already sitting at the wheel, the engine running.

"You and Fiona can sit in the cab with Uncle Mafu, we'll all ride on the back."

He opened the passenger door and Fiona climbed in. I hesitated.

"Tomasi, there's something I've wanted to do since I've been in Tonga. Would you mind if I rode on the back of the truck with all of you?"

"Are you sure? It's not comfortable."

"I'll be fine. I've never ridden in the back of a pickup truck and I really want to; it's not allowed in my country."

I hopped up next to the eight young Tongans, and we jolted across the field. It was such a special experience riding with them although we couldn't converse as I was concentrating on not toppling out. My bottom experienced the shape of every crater as we headed up the road.

They dropped us at the hotel. I realised this was the last time we were going to see Tomasi, and I thought back to when I had first met him at Hawaiian check-in.

"Can I take a photo of all of you please?" I asked.

"Of course," said Tomasi, and like a synchronised dance troupe, the band struck a pose, some of them giving the thumbs-up, and some the *hang loose* hand signal, all of them grinning widely.

I said goodbye to Tomasi, and we returned to our room.

"They were lovely," I said, "and riding in their truck was such a cool experience. There's a real innocence of life in young people here I think we've lost in the West, with health and safety, and violent TV shows, and everything. I hope these guys never lose their joie de vivre."

Fiona hugged me. "You can't solve the world's problems, Simon; change will come to these islands whether we like it or not."

"I know. Anyway, did you have a chat with Mafu while I was bouncing around in the back?"

"I did. I asked him why fewer people were at church today than last week. He said some people don't consider themselves worthy enough to be in the same church as the king. I think that's sad. We're all people, we all eat and sleep and pooh."

"Thank you for putting it that way! Anyway, what would you like to do this afternoon?"

"I'm going to lie down," she said. "I'm feeling a bit funny, I think something at the feast might not have agreed with me."

"Oh, okay, I'll join you. How about some watermelon first? We should use it up as we won't want to take it back with us."

"I don't want to eat anything. You have it."

We spent the afternoon resting, reading, relaxing. I snorkelled off the beach in the late afternoon and followed a school of cuttlefish. I had never seen them alive, only their dead white bones on beaches. They were graceful in the water, expertly displaying their talent for synchronised swimming as if they were practising for the Invertebrate Olympics.

Sunday was cook's night off, so after chips and some more watermelon, we turned in.

≈ ≈ ≈

Linda drove us to Lifuka Island Airport.

A small wooden kiosk constituted the departure area.

It had a hatch in the centre, with little double doors opening outwards.

On the left-hand side of the hatch in red paint was handwritten the word *Check*.

On the right-hand side of the hatch in red paint was handwritten the word *In*.

We approached the hatch and found the airport manager looking out.

"Leaving so soon?" he asked.

"Yes, we're returning to Nuku'alofa for a while."

"Too busy for me. I don't like big cities."

Given Nuku'alofa had a population of around 20,000, I wondered how he'd cope in London.

We handed him our tickets, printed all those months ago by Ben at Travel Unlimited.

"Please place your bags on the scales," he said.

"Scales? What scales?" I asked.

He pointed and exited his kiosk via a side door.

A giant circular white dial on a stand with a rectangular metal foot stood to the left of his hut. A brass label advertised the scale had last seen active service on Paddington Station. Around the base embossed letters proudly announced it had been *Made in Britain.*

A coin slot on the front requested an old British penny, the fee on the railway platform if a passenger wished to discover how heavy they were. This dated the scale as pre-1971 decimalisation.

I placed our first bag on the metal foot and the airport manager inserted one pre-decimal British penny. The penny clunked into the coin collection container, and the needle on the scale showed my bag weighed 23lb. The airport manager retrieved the coin, repeated the process with our second bag, and took us back to his kiosk. I wondered how he'd manage if he ever lost his penny.

We watched him writing.

He wrote a lot of words.

He handed us our boarding passes.

Royal Tongan Airlines was printed at the top, but the boxes for our names, the flight number, our seat numbers, even whether we were smoking, or non-smoking, had all been completed in the airport manager's neat handwriting.

We were the only passengers being picked up in Ha'apai.

A distant buzzing advertised the plane's approach. We looked towards the sound and watched the tiny dot grow bigger.

The airport manager pushed our bags on his trolley and strode on to the runway. He started his livestock removal drill, and pigs scattered into the bushes at his yells.

He stood to one side of the runway and waved at the pilot as the plane landed, the same plane we'd arrived on. It stopped and turned round in a tight circle, its engine noise reduced, and the propellors idled to a stop.

The three steps extended.

The pilot stepped out and shook hands with the airport manager.

He opened the hatch in the back of the plane and threw our bags in.

We showed the pilot our boarding passes and climbed up, occupying the last two available seats.

As the plane ascended, the town of Pangai passed below us. We flew over the island of Uoleva, and I could identify Mark's yacht. I wondered how Mark and Rupert were getting on with their plans. I wondered what Kapo, and Sebastian, and the piglets, and the dogs, and Rascal the cat were up to today.

Then all we could see was the ocean, with a smattering of islets.

≈ ≈ ≈

As Kesi drove us back into the built-up area, we understood what the airport manager had meant when he said he didn't like big cities. After spending time in the pristine islands of Ha'apai, Nuku'alofa was Los Angeles.

Toni leant on the door, rolling a cigarette.

"Welcome back guys, how was your holiday?"

"Wonderful, Toni," I said, "an incredible place. So remote."

"Oh dear, you've adapted to Tongan life. Wait until you land in New Zealand, it'll be like going to a metropolis. I've put you back in the same room, hope that's okay."

"Great, thanks Toni, and we'll grab our bags out of your cupboard too if we can."

We collapsed on the bed surrounded by luggage.

Fiona stretched and yawned. "Buy some food, then siesta?"

"Yes, and you know what we can do this evening? We should go to the cinema. Remember Isy in Hawaii recommended it for the experience."

"All right, we'll find it and discover what's on."

We pulled some clean clothes from the luggage in the cupboard and headed out.

The cinema advertised *A Time to Kill*, an adaptation of a John Grisham novel I had read some years previously.

"What's it about?" asked Fiona.

"As far as I remember, it's about racism in the Deep South of America, and how one black man takes revenge against white people who rape his little girl."

"I'm not sure I want to see that; it doesn't sound like my kind of thing."

"Well, there's nothing else on, and it's only two pa'anga each. If you find it too gruesome, we can always leave. It starts at 7.30, let's come back and buy tickets later."

We picked up a few groceries at Morris Hedstrom supermarket, and returned to Toni's for an afternoon lie down.

It was so hot, even the dogs were speechless.

≈ ≈ ≈

The flickering unreliable streetlights showed us the way back to the cinema. I was thinking about Isy all that time ago in Hawaii, and how he'd said the movie itself wasn't the principal attraction of going to the cinema in Tonga. We were about to find out what was.

We paid the two pa'anga and entered the deserted theatre.

"Where do you want to sit, Fiona?"

"No idea, Simon. Every seat in this row is broken."

"Try the next one. Nope, they're all broken too."

"Here's one that works. Let's see if we can find a pair."

We found two complete seats, with a broken one between them.

"Well, this is romantic." Fiona laughed and reached for my hand across the broken middle seat. "I wonder where everyone else will sit?"

Around 7.30, several Tongan families arrived, conversing all at once and struggling under the weight of the belongings they were carrying, heavy shopping bags, blankets, some of them had brought their own chairs.

They spread their possessions over the floor amongst the broken cinema seats and unloaded their bags. It wasn't unlike the feast in Ha'apai. The smell of hot food drifted over to us, and I hoped the noise of their conversation would die down when the film started. They laughed, and the men slapped each other's backs. The cinema was merely a venue for a Tongan social event.

The film started.

The conversation continued.

We tried to concentrate on the film.

We were getting to the crux of the story.

Samuel L. Jackson burst out of the courtroom cupboard and shot the two white rapists dead.

"Oooooooooooooooooh" said all the Tongans, noticing the movie at last.

The deputies moved in to arrest him, and the film slowed down and ground to a halt. The screen showed a shadow of stretched celluloid.

"Aaaawwwwww," said all the Tongans, returning to their family discussions.

The cinema plunged into darkness.

Fiona squeezed my hand. "I hope they can get it going again. It's a bit scary in here."

A few minutes later the screen flickered, and the film restarted. The Tongans all cheered. The rapists came back to life, and Samuel L. Jackson burst out of the cupboard and killed them again. This time they stayed dead.

The Tongans quietened as the film progressed. I wondered if they had any cognizance of life in Mississippi, the history of slavery, and the underbelly of ongoing racism the film portrayed.

My question was soon answered.

On the screen, a horde of Ku Klux Klan members marched down a street, intent on avenging the deaths of the white rapists. Anonymous hoods with holes for eyes topped their flowing white robes.

They represented pure evil.

35.
Gate Two

The Tongans found the Ku Klux Klan's appearance hilarious.

Unrestrained laughter filled the cinema.

The Klan advanced, holding their burning torches.

The Tongans laughed louder.

They'd no idea what they were watching.

My emotions were torn between sadness they didn't appreciate the seriousness of the film's message, and pleasure they lived lives innocent and sheltered from such evil doctrines.

Isy had been right. When you go to the cinema in Tonga, the principal attraction isn't the film.

≈ ≈ ≈

"Pok pok pok."

"Pok."

"Pok pok pok pok pok."

The chickens' reception committee formally received us back to Nuku'alofa.

"Last full day in Tonga, Fiona," I said, "the time's gone so quickly."

"I know, I can't believe I'm going to be with Mum and Dad tomorrow after over two years."

"We still haven't seen the queen. I'm so disappointed we've missed her."

"I'm sorry," said Fiona. "At least you saw the king; you were even in the same church as him. He's Queen Sālote's son, isn't that more important than seeing the queen?"

"I suppose so. I just had this thing about the queen. I so wanted to see her."

Fiona changed the subject. "I need to do a bit of shopping before we leave."

"You and your shopping, don't we have enough to carry?"

"I haven't bought many presents for my family. I was thinking of getting something traditionally Tongan. They've never been to any of the Pacific islands; a gift from here will be unique."

"Okay, sounds good. We should also change some travellers' cheques into New Zealand dollars. We'll need some money at Auckland airport, there's a couple of hours before our flight on to Christchurch."

The Vatican's gift stall would have been proud to stock the extensive range of Christian crafts displayed in the Friendly Islands Bookshop. Fiona's family weren't religious, so we dismissed most of the items for sale, and ended up with some napkin rings carved in the shape of tropical fish. We bought a book with photos of Tonga, none of which had been taken much after 1960.

We returned to Toni's to pack for our early morning flight and sat in the communal area playing cards.

Toni walked in.

"Hello you two, I've organised a bit of a surprise for your last night."

"You have?" I asked.

"Yep, I'm going to do a kava evening. And because there aren't any Tongans here, the ladies can join in too."

He produced a round kava bowl on stumpy legs, a smaller version of the one I had seen at the feast in Ha'apai. This time I had no concern about following protocol.

An Australian called John, and Nicole the doctor joined us, and we all sat in a circle on the floor. Toni pounded the bag of kava in water until it turned the familiar colour of dirty dishwater. He produced a yellow plastic ladle and gave us each a half coconut. There was no ceremony of passing round the circle here. We each sipped some kava and talked.

Nicole regaled us with her experiences at the hospital, explaining how many of the older Tongans refused her insistence that they take western medicine, preferring traditional cures. John had returned from a remote island called 'Eua, and had some interesting tales. It sounded even more primitive than the Ha'apai Islands.

We shared our stories about the king, the feast, Mark's yacht, in the convivial kava circle spirit. Kava still didn't make me feel the slightest bit light-headed, but I was going to miss Tonga and all my new friends very much.

≈ ≈ ≈

I forgave the chickens for waking us up this final morning. I was even going to miss their pok-pok-pokking.

How will I ever adjust to the western world again?

Kesi drove us to the airport.

There was a lot of activity outside the terminal. I remembered what the check-in lady had said, it was busiest when Air New Zealand came in. Families were farewelling their departing relatives, off to earn the big bucks in Auckland so they could send money home. Police and other officials meandered around, more than might seem necessary for a regular day.

We hugged Kesi goodbye. I wanted to cry.

"Bye, Kesi," I said.

"Take care of that gorgeous baby of yours," said Fiona.

We turned and faced the terminal, and queued for check-in. The human baggage carousel plucked our bags from the scales.

We sat at the familiar gate one.

The ceiling fans turned slowly.

People arriving for the flight filled the seats.

Fiona read a magazine discarded by another traveller.

I idly flicked through the Tongan guidebook. We'd done so much in the few weeks we'd been here, met so many wonderful people. After the months of planning, I couldn't accept our Tongan expedition was ending.

"Kia ora, Ladies and Gentlemen. Please remain in your seats. We will be boarding shortly."

I looked up and idly glanced over to the other side of the terminal at the disused gate two.

Gate two.

Not disused.

Gate two was open.

A contingent of smartly dressed Tongan men stood at gate two, flanked by three policemen, hands behind their backs.

"Fiona, what's going on at gate two? Something's happening."

I stood up and walked as closely towards the second gate as I dared, without drawing attention to myself. Fiona appeared at my elbow.

The doors from the gate out to the tarmac were open. A well-worn red carpet ran through them. Ropes stretched between small chrome stands at the edge.

We stood and watched.

Nothing happened.

We waited. Other people were looking.

I turned to a Tongan airport worker close to me.

"What's going on?" I asked.

"It'll be the king or the queen. They keep gate two for the royal family."

Wow.

A few more minutes passed. I needed the toilet, but I wasn't leaving.

The police stood to attention. A group of well-dressed people swept in and paused at the end of the red carpet. One official stepped forward, approached the group, and bowed in front of a lady in the centre.

"Fiona, it's the queen, the Queen of Tonga! It's Queen Hala-vala whatsername. It's her!"

I shuffled forward as close to the red carpet as I dared.

The official led the queen and her entourage down the red carpet, through the small chrome rope stands. The queen waved and smiled at the Tongan onlookers, as he escorted her towards the open doors of gate two.

She passed us.

In disbelief, I waved at her.

She looked right at me.

She smiled and waved.

Slow motion.

I'll remember this moment for ever. Me and the Queen of Tonga. Just me and her.

The entourage continued through the open doors.

"Simon, are you okay?"

I hugged Fiona.

"Can you believe it?" I said, "that was the queen. The Queen of Tonga. We actually laid eyes on her. I can't wait to call Dad and tell him."

I watched the rear of her group disappear up the steps of the plane.

"Not just that, Simon, she'll be on the same plane as us to New Zealand. I'm sure she'll be in first class though."

"This is amazing. Wait there, I have to go for a pee."

I returned from the toilets to find other passengers queueing to board.

"They're boarding first and business, Simon. We'll be next."

"Fiona, pinch me. I saw the Queen of Tonga. I saw her, and she waved at me."

"It's incredible isn't it, Simon. You must be so pleased."

"I, wow, I, I, damn."

"What?"

"We didn't take a photo."

"Oh well, you'll always remember this, you don't need a photo. Come on, let's join the queue."

The Air New Zealand plane welcomed us into its westernised embrace. We'd no plans, little money, no jobs, and no visible future. We'd no idea where our adventures would take us next.

I didn't care.

All was right with the world. I had seen the Queen of Tonga, and she had smiled.

Epilogue
Where Are They Now?

Thank you very much for reading the first in my series of travel memoirs, *South Pacific Shenanigans*. I've kept up with many of the characters in the book, and I thought you might be interested to know what's happened in their lives since 1996.

Ben, the travel agent, lost his job when Travel Unlimited merged with another company. He moved to New Zealand with his Kiwi girlfriend, where, in a complete coincidence, they discovered they were living in the same Auckland street as the King and Queen of Tonga.

Bob Fletcher passed away, and is remembered as one of the greatest showmen ever. His son Troy now upholds his legacy at Fletcher's Steam Fair.

Toni still runs Toni's Guest House in Nuku'alofa, (tonisguesthouse.com) and still organises kava evenings for backpackers. Kesi and her husband Vili have sadly both died, but baby Toni is now a strapping rugby prop forward.

Nils and Claudia married and returned to Tonga, where they ran a bar for a while, before emigrating again to Germany. They have two children, both of whom have German names and are bilingual. Nobody has heard from Anja.

Nicole, the doctor, returned to her native Perth, Australia, where she practices medicine and is a mother to three very clever children.

Kapo Folau has retired from owning The Bounty Resort. He spends his days reflecting on his time spent on the island, and still manages to avoid going to church.

And Fiona and me? Well, we've had plenty more adventures, and you'll be able to read about them in the next *South Pacific Shenanigans* book. If you'd like to sign up to my mailing list, you'll be the first to find out when this is released. Feel free to register by visiting **simonmichaelprior.com**

Please review *The Coconut Wireless*

Thank you for reading my book, I hope you enjoyed it as much as I enjoyed writing it. Would you please consider leaving a review? Even just a few words would help others decide if the book is right for them.

I've made it super simple: just copy this link into your web browser and you'll travel to the Amazon review page for this book where you can leave your review.

Best regards, and thank you in advance:

Smarturl.it/Coconutreview

Photos to accompany *The Coconut Wireless*

If you'd like to see some of our photos that accompany the scenes in *The Coconut Wireless*, please head over to my website at **simonmichaelprior.com**, and click the picture of the book's cover.

Disclaimer

I have tried to recreate events, locales, and conversations from my memories of them. To maintain their anonymity, in some instances I have changed the names of individuals and places. I may have changed some identifying characteristics and details such as physical properties, occupations, and places of residence. Any mistakes are all my own work. SMP.

About the Author

Simon Michael Prior insists on inflicting all aspects of life on himself so that his readers can enjoy learning about his latest trip / experience / disaster / emotional breakdown (insert phrase of your choice).

During his extended adolescence, now over forty years long, he has lived on two boats and sunk one of them; sold houses, street signs, Indian food and paper bags for a living; visited almost fifty countries and lived in three; qualified as a scuba divemaster; nearly killed himself learning to wakeboard; trained as a search and rescue skipper with the Coast Guard, and built his own house without the benefit of an instruction manual.

Simon is as amazed as anyone that the house is still standing, and he now lives in it by the sea with his wife and twin daughters, where he spends his time regurgitating his experiences on paper before he has so many more that he forgets them.

Website: **simonmichaelprior.com**

Email: **simon@simonmichaelprior.com**
Facebook: **@simonmichaelprior**
Instagram: **@simonmichaelprior**
Twitter: **@simonmichaelpri**

If you would like to receive a regular newsletter about Simon and his writing, and be the first to find out about new releases, please sign up to his mailing list here:

simonmichaelprior.com/#signup

Other books by Simon Michael Prior

Have you ever wanted a first-hand glimpse into post-war 1940s New York? When 21-year-old John Miskin Prior travelled by ship to New York in 1948, he had no idea he was going to meet and dine with the Roosevelts and the Rockefellers. No idea he would be among the first ever to see 'South Pacific' and 'Death of a Salesman'. No idea he would witness Truman's election victory, so unexpected, the newspapers were reprinted.

This eyewitness account of an English student living in New York for the incredible year of 1948 – 49 has been collated from his letters discovered after his death, and forms a unique account of the period.

Available on Simon's website at:

simonmichaelprior.com

Acknowledgements

A big thank you to Victoria Twead and all the members of the Facebook group 'We Love Memoirs', for befriending me, encouraging me, educating me, reassuring me, and driving me forward. Thank you to Jacky Donovan, for being my guide, my mentor and for stopping me from making a lot of stupid mistakes. Thank you to Beth Haslam and Annemarie Rawson for taking the time to give me your advice, guidance and for being a shoulder when I needed it. Thank you to my beta readers: Alyson Sheldrake, Liesbet Collaert, Kevin J D Kelly, Susan Jackson, and Pauline Armstrong. You guys rock; your feedback was spot on, and I learned a lot from our journey together. Thank you to David Gaughran and Dave Chesson for informative courses, tips and useful tools. Thank you to Jeff Bezos, for giving independent authors a platform on which to publish our writing. And thank you so much to Fiona, I couldn't have done it without you.

We Love Memoirs

Join me and other memoir authors and readers in the 'We Love Memoirs' Facebook group, the friendliest group on Facebook.

www.facebook.com/groups/welovememoirs

CPSIA information can be obtained
at www.ICGtesting.com
Printed in the USA
LVHW040737210523
747596LV00012B/74